ANCIENT CAMBODIAN SCULPTURE

Fig. 1   Temple of Angkor Vat, twelfth century.

Ancient Cambodian Sculpture

Sherman E. Lee

THE ASIA SOCIETY INC. Distributed by New York Graphic Society Ltd.

Ancient Cambodian Sculpture is the catalogue of an exhibition selected by Dr. Sherman E. Lee, Director of The Cleveland Museum of Art, and shown in the Asia House Gallery in the fall of 1969 as an activity of The Asia Society, to further greater understanding between the United States and the peoples of Asia.

An Asia House Gallery Publication

Printed in England

Library of Congress Catalogue Card Number: 79-86374

Fig. 10A Tympanum, Banteay Srei temple, second half of the tenth century. *Detail*.

Contents

Fig. 2 Temple of Bayon, Angkor Thom, late twelfth–early thirteenth century.

Preface

We owe our relatively comprehensive understanding of Cambodian art to the French. Their archaeological and scholarly commitment to the ancient products of their former dependency was sealed by the formation of the École Française d'Extrême-Orient in Hanoi in 1898,[1] and the numerous excavations and publications of that scholastic brotherhood are the corpus upon which all students have, do, and will build their studies. The opening of The Musée Guimet in 1879 in Lyons by Mr. Guimet[2] and its later development in Paris of collections of Cambodian art provided Westerners with a Cambodian home abroad. Where Chinese, Japanese, and Indian art were known but frag-
mentarily, illuminated by a flickering light like that of Plato's cave, the art of the ancient Khmer empire was represented by a more or less complete series of sculptures, even including such large architectural elements as a fronton (tympanum) from Banteay Srei, or groups of carved lintels from major sites covering over six hundred years of development. Even such direct experience of Cambodian works as existed in the United States before the thirties of this century was largely due to the artistic and scholarly cooperation of the École Française, which provided The Metropolitan Museum of Art with a documented series of major sculptures in 1936.[3] Representation of Cambodian art in other American

---

[1] Then known as Mission Archéologique d'Indochine. The name was changed in 1900.
[2] In 1888 the museum was moved to Paris.

[3] Alan Priest, "A Collection of Cambodian Sculpture," *Bulletin of the Metropolitan Museum of Art*, vol XXXII, No. 4 (April 1937), pp. 84–88.

museums was fragmentary if it existed at all. The American contribution to Cambodian studies symbolizes the state of affairs to date—no major publication on Cambodian art has appeared in this country, and only one historical study of any substance, that by Lawrence Palmer Briggs.[4]

The situation with regard to monuments and scholarship is paralleled by that in popular appreciation. The Paris World's Fair of 1900 had its quarter-scale replica of Angkor Vat and its troupe of Royal Cambodian dancers. The early escapades of André Malraux in Cambodia[5] were only the most visible of numerous comparable French efforts to possess the aesthetic wealth of this part of the romantic and mysterious East, efforts often crowned with success to judge from the copious holdings of French private collections, some of them later dispersed to the New World. If travel to Angkor was common for the cultured citizen of France, it was an extremely exotic foray for an American. The second World War changed all this and the noticeably improved guest facilities at Angkor are material evidence of the growing influx of visitors to this wonder from all affluent areas of the world. With increasing familiarity came galloping collectivitis, and hence the possibility of an exhibition of Cambodian sculpture drawn almost wholly from American collections.

There has been one major problem in our understanding of Cambodian art. Just as we first knew of Chinese painting through Japanese eyes, often our view of the products of the Khmer sculptor has been through Siamese eyes. The aesthetic situation may well have been conditioned by the political one. In any case, many non-Cambodian works in Cambodian style have been assimilated to an assumed Cambodian corpus. Siamese art has its own virtues, but they are not those of its eastern neighbor. One of the purposes of the present display is to rectify this peculiarly American vision of Cambodian art—in short to show the sculpture of Cambodia "sui generis," for in his pure and original creations the ancient Cambodian sculptor may have peers, but no superiors.

No effort has been made here to provide a true summary of Cambodian art. For that, one is referred to the Selected Bibliography, particularly to the books by Coral de Rémusat and by Groslier and Arthaud. The present author acknowledges this text as a kind of personal memoir for an exhibition which has given him as much delight in assembling as he hopes it may provide the visitor.

Particular thanks and credit must be given to Mr. Stanislaw Czuma, Ford Foundation Internee at The Cleveland Museum of Art, who was my principal assistant in preparing the exhibition, particularly in developing and refining the catalogue entries. William E. Ward was most helpful in providing the maps and designing the chronological chart. Mrs. Janet Grasso typed the manuscript. The staff of the Asia House Gallery, especially its Director, Mr. Gordon Washburn, and Miss Virginia Field and Mr. Jack Spinx, were continuously helpful at all stages of the exhibition.

SHERMAN E. LEE
Director, The Cleveland Museum of Art

---

[4]Bibl. 9.
[5]See Malraux's novel, *La Voie Royale* (The Royal Way), trans. Stuart Gilbert (New York, 1935), pp. 96 ff., a fictional recounting of his activities in Indo-China in the twenties.

Acknowledgments

It is thanks to the generous friends and supporters of The Asia Society, who are concerned with the continuance of these events, that the exhibitions of the Asia House Gallery take place. Their initiator and constant supporter is John D. Rockefeller 3rd, whose foundation of our society and its activities constitutes a unique benefaction. Equally vital to these events are the notable specialists in Asian art who, at our invitation, choose the works of art that are displayed and compose the catalogues that accompany each exhibition. Theirs is a precious gift to us of time and knowledge that can never be adequately acknowledged.

In this instance, we are indebted to Dr. Sherman E. Lee, Director of The Cleveland Museum of Art and a distinguished scholar in the field of Asian art, for making a major exhibition possible. Dr. Lee generously helped with the first exhibition presented by the Asia House Gallery in 1960, as a member of the Committee who chose "Masterpieces of Asian Art in American Collections." In 1960, he also selected the miniatures and wrote the catalogue for "Rajput Painting" at the request of

George Montgomery, our Gallery's director. Three years later, he conceived the idea of "Tea Taste in Japanese Art," choosing its displays as well as writing the illuminating book that served as its catalogue.

Now, Dr. Lee has made a selection of ancient Cambodian sculpture that indicates the surprising richness of our American collections today. Although this is our second showing of Khmer sculpture (the first having taken place in 1961), the decade that has passed has been a remarkable one for discovery and acquisition, as the exhibition so clearly testifies.

As may be seen from the list of lenders, a considerable number of private owners as well as of public museums have permitted us to borrow their fine works for this event—an exhibition that we hope may encourage many more travelers to visit the marvelous remains of the great Khmer civilization in Cambodia, the original sites from which these treasures have come.

GORDON BAILEY WASHBURN
Director, Asia House Gallery

8

Lenders

The George P. Bickford Collection, Cleveland

Center of Asian Art and Culture,
    City and County of San Francisco;
    Avery Brundage Collection

Albright-Knox Art Gallery, Buffalo

The Art Institute of Chicago

The Cleveland Museum of Art

The Denver Art Museum

The Detroit Institute of Arts

Dr. and Mrs. Samuel Eilenberg, New York

R. Hatfield Ellsworth and James R. Goldie,
    New York

Fogg Art Museum, Harvard University, Cambridge

Mr. Georges Halphen, La Chapelle en Serval
    (Oise)

Mr. and Mrs. Ben Heller, New York

Mr. I. Kahane, Dobbs Ferry, N.Y.

Kimbell Art Foundation, Fort Worth

Mr. Peter Marks, New York

The Metropolitan Museum of Art, New York

Museum of Fine Arts, Boston

Nelson-Atkins Gallery, Kansas City, Mo.

Philadelphia Museum of Art

Mr. and Mrs. John D. Rockefeller 3rd, New York

Mr. Robert Rousset, Paris

Seattle Art Museum

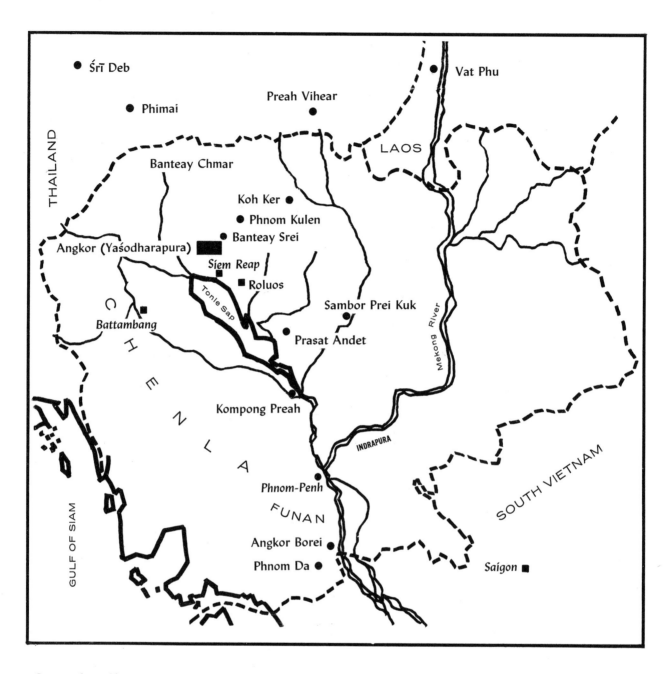

Cambodia

Cambodian Sculpture

Cambodia was never a mammoth empire. Even at its greatest extent under Jayavarman VII, when Champa (present-day Viet-Nam) became a Khmer province in 1203, the area effectively dominated by a Cambodian culture was not much more than 200,000 square miles, the size of present-day France. Yet in this area, further restricted by the requirements of transportation by waterways, hundreds of imposing monuments, occasionally Buddhist but usually Hindu, were built between c. 650 AD and c. 1250. These ranged from early, single-cell, brick shrines to elaborate, storied complexes such as Angkor Vat and the Bayon (Figs. 1 and 2). Nearly all were profusely decorated with ornamental or figural sculpture in relief, and peopled with numerous images in the round. Given the population support-able by the land, and six hundred years, the mere quantity of monumental construction and carving is prodigious. One can only conclude that the making of monuments was, with war and public order, the principal activity of the state as embodied in the God-King, the cult of the realm derived from the Indianized Śrīvijaya Empire of Java, Sumatra, and Malaya. The cult of the God-King, with all of its implications of theocracy, absolutism and total dedication of the state to the cult, made the divine character of any official construction inevitable. As in Egypt, the full weight of controlled society was at the service of the god and his representative on earth; monuments could not be erected often enough to satisfy the needs of the unseen powers. The long continuation of a simple agricultural and foraging

Fig. 3   Vishnu, style of Phnom Da, sixth century, National Museum, Phnom Penh. *Upper left.*
Fig. 4   Harihara, style of Prasat Andet, first half of the eighth century. National Museum, Phnom Penh. *Upper right.*
Fig. 5   The battle of Kuruksetra warriors, Angkor Vat relief, twelfth century.

economy preserved the sharp dichotomy of rulers and peasantry. The massed labor force, including large numbers of slaves, with but few commercial activities, was at the service of the deified monarch. If the quantity of work produced is staggering, the corollary is that it varies widely in quality. This is especially true in those periods of particularly massive construction projects, the early tenth century (Koh Ker and Bakheng styles), and the twelfth and early thirteenth centuries (Angkor Vat and the Bayon). Contrariwise, the earliest works of the sixth and seventh centuries present a very high level of consistency and quality, as products of an emerging aristocratic culture dedicated to newly-appeared and fervently worshipped Buddhist and Hindu deities but recently imported from India.

The appearance and quality of these images (Nos. 1–8) is so particular, so consistent, and so different from the rest of Cambodian art as to require special consideration. Aside from the often mysterious wide-lipped smile and a penchant for representing the figure in the full round, there is little in these "pre-Angkor" works that anticipates the classic expressions of Cambodian style from the ninth to the thirteenth centuries, a continuously unfolding body of work, consistent in stylistic development, iconography and technique. The consistency of the pre-Angkor sculptures is evidenced

through varied types of images and for a relatively short time—the sixth to the eighth centuries. The term, pre-Angkor, now generally accepted as designating these works, implies the same meaning as the now discarded term "pre-Khmer"—that is, works produced before the unification of the lower and upper Mekong river areas (the old Chinese-described Funan and Chenla) by Jayavarman II in 802, but more particularly, before the movement of the capital to Angkor by Yasovarman at the end of the ninth century. The implication that these sculptures antedate at least the formation of a true Cambodian style, and even the existence of a Cambodian cultural hegemony is surely correct. Despite details, even flavors, that anticipate the future, the stylistic integrity of the group is both pre-Angkor and pre-Khmer.

Disregarding the valid, if specialized, differentiations of style within the pre-Angkor group, established by Dupont, Boisselier and others,[1] the some forty stone sculptures shown here generally share certain major preoccupations. In contrast to Indian works which are rarely conceived in the round, the pre-Khmer figures are almost all worked in the full round, whether viewed from front and back, the four quarters, or far more rarely, from all possible views within three hundred and sixty

---

[1] Bibl. 20, pls. IV, VII.

Fig. 6   Dancing apsaras, pillar relief from Bayon temple, late twelfth–early thirteenth century.
Fig. 7   Dancing apsaras, pillar relief from Bayon temple, late twelfth–early thirteenth century.

degrees. The latter approach is unusual since the sculptures require supporting members in the form of struts and mandorlas (body-halos) to overcome the brittleness and instability of the unsupported stone representation of the human figure in the round. This is especially true for the pre-Khmer group because of the second peculiarity they share in common, the careful, sensitive, and observant attention to anatomic detail, even tear-ducts (Fig.3), but particularly to the articulation of the body. Were the sculptors less aware of these requirements, the ankles and legs could be less thin, less natural, more like some of their Indian prototypes or their later classic Cambodian descendants. Collarbones (Fig. 4), elbows, knees and ankles are especially well rendered and are elegant in profile and detail. The slender legs and ankles particularly mitigate against stable use of the stone, and hence the need for supports. Greek and Baroque sculptors wrestled with the same problems but cloaked their solutions by naturalistic excuses and details—tree trunks, drapery, rearing animals, etc. The Indians obliterated joints in the body, achieving an organic flow of flesh into flesh; and they usually conceived of sculpture, even in iconic form, as issuing from a solid stone background, at least until the Medieval (eighth–twelfth century) regional styles, which could have had no influence on the pre-Angkor images.

Yet another characteristic of this early style is the remarkably subtle and technically refined handling of the skin of the stone. Many of the pieces, whether executed in sandstone or limestone, have a polished surface producing a taut effect—the stone within the skin. This practice has a corollary. Drapery is usually incised or carved in very low relief, disturbing the surface tension of the finished stone surface as little as possible. This too is unlike the usual Indian practice. The general effect of these unique pre-Angkor characteristics, combined with the characteristics shared with and derived from India, is that of a strongly architectonic, intellectual framework within which there exists a marvelously refined sensuality, restrained here but anticipating the broader and more explicit sensuality of classic Cambodian production.

But how can this all have happened so early in Funan and Chenla, later the "Chenla of the water and the Chenla of the land"?[2] *The prior culture of the region was an amalgam of "primitive" with bronze age elements derived from Han China—the Dong-son culture of Southeast Asia, particularly Indochina. Certainly there were no iconographic or technical precedents for this highly developed figural art. The subjects of the new sculptural style, Buddhist and Hindu, clearly point to a pre-*

[2] Bibl. 9, p. 58.

15

dominantly Indian origin. But when we say this we are confronted with a host of problems and possibilities. Local inscriptions of the period include Western Indian, Deccani and early Pallava type scripts. The cylindrical miter of the Vishnu and Lakshmi figures is found in a pure form in such early Pallava sites as the Mahisha Mandapa at Mamallapuram and in decorated form at Aihole and Bādāmi in the Deccan. The pre-Angkor Buddha images (No. 3) and even some of the Hindu figures (Nos. 6, 7) are closely related to sixth-century phases of the Gupta style of Sarnath, such as the Sarnath Padmapani,[3] or the slightly earlier Berlin Balarāma from Mathura.[4] The short undergarments with incised or low relief drapery lines are common in sculptures from Deogarh, c. 600.[5]

But then there are other, less direct possibilities. Some of the closest parallels to both male and female pre-Angkor sculptures are to be found in such rare early stones from Nepal as that of a King (?) and the Devi from an earlier Asia Society exhibition.[6] While it is highly unlikely that there are any direct connections between Nepal and Cambodia, what is interesting is that both were borrowing from a common source at the same time, and the Nepalese sources were the Gupta and immediately post-Gupta idioms from Northern India and Bengal. Even further afield is a probably fanciful, but intriguing, derivation of pre-Angkor linearity in indicating details of drapery from exposure to Chinese sculpture of the northern Ch'i and Sui dynasties. These columnar figures with their subtle, surface-indicated drapery lines must have been known to the aristocracy of Funan and Chenla through their numerous embassies to China, which, with Chinese records, provide most of our historical documentation for this early period in the Mekong region. A supporting clue can be drawn from the curious fact that many epigraphists agree on the technical and aesthetic superiority of early Cambodian Sanskrit inscriptions, whether in Pallava or early Chālukyan script.[7] Why should newcomers to a hallowed Indian art so easily and quickly surpass their mentors at the linear and proportional problems of incised inscriptions? Could Chinese linear discipline have had some echoing effect?

This cloudy kaleidoscope of influences, real or imagined, actually provides a very clear answer to the vexing problem of the origins of this extraordinary sculptural art. We must imagine an

[3] Heinrich Zimmer, *The Art of Indian Asia*, vol. II (New York, 1955), pl. 108a.

[4] *Indische Kunst* (Stuttgart/Hamburg, 1966), No. 50.

[5] *Ibid.*, No. 53; Zimmer, *op. cit.*, pl. 111.

[6] Stella Kramrisch, *Art of Nepal* (Asia House Gallery exhibition catalogue, New York, 1964), nos. 1 and 2; the latter should be compared with our No. 4 and with Bibl. 22, Fig. 278.

[7] Barth as quoted in Bibl. 9, p. 55.

emerging aristocracy of wealth and power, fervent in their preoccupation with the new-found Buddhist and Hindu faiths and their material embodiment in images—objects of worship—rather than in large temples or other tokens of luxury and display, and deluged with imported concrete manifestations of their newly embraced faiths and culture. These things came from India, largely by sea, and were probably small, portable images, usually of metal, from various centers of the faiths in all parts of India. The resulting, almost chaotic, possibilities were refined and solidified by ruling groups, with inexorable will and purpose. The results are their aesthetic justification.

There is still the matter of the polished surfaces and the supporting struts and halos. The polish may well derive from Gupta sculptures of the Sarnath type, often very smoothly finished though not highly polished as was the work of Maurya craftsmen. But perhaps these, too, can be explained by local exposure to imported Indian bronzes. Such metal sculptures have largely disappeared in India, but they must have been more common than now, particularly in the early styles we are discussing. In these models, with their shiny, polished surfaces, their casting techniques made visible in the strut-channels[8] and encircling mandorlas, and with

their tightly contained draperies, the early Cambodian sculptors had visual inspirations which could be transformed into stone—or into bronze itself. Before the last war, pre-Khmer sculpture in metal was known largely in small and relatively crude examples, though Buddhist bronzes of large size and wonderful quality, from the region of Amaravati during the era of the Sātavāhana dynasts (235 BC–AD 225), had been found in Southeast Asia.[9] Now some important, large, and beautiful bronzes, both Buddhist and Hindu, have appeared (No. 8) adding greatly to our knowledge and understanding of pre-Khmer art. For bronze, then of high importance, was used in large images, and presented in a masterful and homogeneous style, derived from India yet different from the sculpture of that country. Why not a close relationship between the primary source metal and the dominant result, stone? Like most of the metal images, some of the earliest of the stone sculptures (No. 1) make provision for inlaid eyes of a different material. These mixed and varied strains at the beginnings of Cambodian art were quickly unified into an unmistakably new genus, and this new strain, in turn, provided the origins for classic Cambodian art.

A few of these seeds were important elements in the pre-Angkor style. The concept of the single

[8] R. D. Banerji, "Eastern Indian School of Mediaeval Sculpture," *Archeological Survey of India*, n.s. vol. XLVII (1933), pl. Ic.

[9] *Art and Archeology of Vietnam* (Smithsonian Institution traveling exhibition catalogue, Washington, D.C., 1961), p. 2.

Fig. 8   Towers of the Bayon temple, late twelfth–early thirteenth century.
Fig. 9   Statue of the "Leper King," Angkor Thom, late twelfth–early thirteenth century.

image in the round remained until the end of Cambodian art. One could almost say that the identification of the deity with the king, whether in the form of Vishnu, Śiva, or the Buddhist Lokeśvara, precluded any daring innovation. It was a magical formula not to be tampered with, in contrast to the inventiveness displayed in the decorative and figural sculpture in relief. The smile, too, was an integral part of the early style and was continued, broadened, and made into a major motif. The nudity of the upper torso, in contrast to Indian and Chinese sculpture, remained as an undiminished image of physical well-being and spiritual health, despite the jeweled encroachments of the twelfth and thirteenth centuries and the Buddha's monkish garment of the same time. On the other hand, the "sampot," the short covering of masculine loins, and the longer, ankle-length skirt of the females, so lightly sketched in the pre-Angkor group, develops into the major ornament of the figure in later Cambodian art. One detail, the "fish-tail" or "anchor" drapery started by accident in India,[10] and more intentionally in the pre-Angkor figures,[11] becomes a "leit-motiv" of later sculpture, so omnipresent that its variations and ramifications, along with others beloved of the École archaeologists, be-

come almost calendrical devices for a presumed minutely accurate chronology. The "fish-tail" drapery originates in two forms, the one small and detailed, a hanging fold of cloth, the other (No. 4) a large sculptural motif usually seen on female figures, not unknown in India,[12] but never exploited there in the clear manner of later Cambodia (No. 27).

The transition from the pre-Angkor style to the first style of Angkor (see chronological chart) was accomplished by the style of Phnom Kulen (Mt. Mahendra) under the founder of the Khmer kingdom, Jayavarman II (d. 850) and his two successors, Jayavarman III (d. 877) and Indravarman I (d. 889). After this the Khmer capital was transferred to Angkor by Yaśovarman I (d. 900), and we can speak of the art of Angkor. The surviving sculptures from the Kulen region are few and owe much to the work of the preceding period. Two developments point the way to early Angkor, both in male figures since we have no identifiable Kulen period female images. The girdle drapery now begins to appear in high relief with broad, carefully rendered pleats; and the supporting halo and struts are gradually eliminated from sculpture in the round, being replaced as supports by a marked

[10] Zimmer, *op. cit.*, 108a.
[11] Bibl. 20, pls. III, VIII, IX, X, XII, XV, XXIV, XLII.

[12] C. Sivaramamurti, *Kalugumalai and Early Pandyan Rock-cut Shrines* (Bombay, 1961), pls. 20, 29.

Fig. 10   Tympanum, Banteay Srei temple, second half of the tenth century. *Upper left.*
Fig. 11   Dvārapāla, Banteay Srei temple, second half of the tenth century. *Upper right.*
Fig. 12   Wall relief, Bayon temple, late twelfth–early thirteenth century.

increase in the amount of stone left in the legs and ankles, producing an effect of squat heaviness in the lower part of the images, characteristic of Cambodian images in the round from this time on. In a purely aesthetic way ("pace" the moralistic archaeologists) the torsos and heads are usually more attractive than the complete figures—but this hardly excuses the sometimes deliberate separation of body from legs.[13]

With the transfer of the capital to Angkor, except for an interlude under Jayavarman IV (928–41) at Koh Ker, the major productions of the Cambodian builders and artists are henceforth to be found in and around this famous city just northwest of the Great Lake (Siem-Reap). Here, the numerous temples and temple complexes combine to form an enormously expanded "Roman Forum" of structures from different reigns, in different manners, but all unified by a commonly accepted style, whether in the carefully ordered temple-mountain ground plans, the profuse use of foliate ornament to fill space, or in the basic components of figural style in sculpture.

Since nearly all the architectural relief sculpture fortunately still remains in place, the present exhibition places undue emphasis on sculptured images in the round, however important this category was to the Cambodians. The few pieces of architectural sculptures (Nos. 9, 18, 40, 41, 42, 60) shown here give only a slight indication of the variety and ingenuity used by the designers and sculptors over a period of four centuries in solving an almost superhuman problem—to cover miles of stone walls with lively and convincing ornamentation. Obviously tradition and precedent had to play a major part in such an undertaking. Even if mind and energy had been equal to the task, time alone required the shortcuts, the technical lubrication, necessary to produce the imposing result. Thus the ease with which French scholars have been able to compartmentalize the architectural units traditionally employed, in additive fashion like pieces of a jig-saw puzzle, in order to assemble an architectural and aesthetic whole. Each of these categories—lintels (Nos.9,18) applied columns, tympani, false doors, and pilasters (No. 60), bas reliefs with scenes (No. 40)—have been faithfully catalogued and arranged in stylistic sequence.[14] *In general there is a movement from high relief in the earliest works (Nos. 9, 18) to lower relief in the later, including what the Italian Renaissance described as "rilievo stiacciato," almost drawing on stone (No. 42). The narra-*

---

[13]The most extreme example is that of the Stoclet *Krishna* (Bibl. 20, pl. V, A, with legs shown in pl. VII, B) the separation not made by Dupont, of course, but by an owner prior to Stoclet.

[14]Bibl. 16.

tive fluency of the latter is well known from the galleries at Angkor Vat, with their scenes from the Vaishnavite texts and from the Rāmāyana and Mahābhārata (Fig. 5). Sculptural variety and the subtly flexible play of varying depths of light and shade are more prominent in the first Angkor style associated with Preah Ko (No. 9), Koh Ker, and Banteay Srei (No. 18). In these the foliate, jungle-inspired ornament omnipresent in classic Cambodian art is presented at the highest artistic level by means of chisel and drill, particularly the latter. But the ornament is almost never just foliate and decorative. The gods and their vehicles, whether Garuda (No. 9), the elephant of Indra (No. 18), or others are always present, re-emphasizing the magical and religious nature of all Cambodian artistic production. In this architectural ornament one sees more easily than anywhere else the gradual movement from a controlled and sophisticated aesthetic to one more akin to folk art, unselfconscious and technically less flexible (No. 41).

Nevertheless one should never underestimate the power of the individual artist at any point in a line of development. This is particularly true in a situation where such a quantity of work was required of the sculptors. A close examination of exactly congruent work at the same place and at the same time (No. 42 and Figs. 6, 7) reveals variations in quality only discernible by comparison, the basic

discipline for qualitative judgment in the arts.

Such persistent acts of comparison are fundamental to the understanding of the variety within the seeming uniformity of figural sculpture of the earlier and later styles of Angkor. The norm had already been suggested by the transitional works of Kulen, where the observant naturalism and unified refinement of the pre-Angkor style had been modified in the direction of a clear separation of parts—head, torso, lower garment, legs—in part achieved by a deeper cutting into the stone representing garment and headdress. The Brahmā (No. 10) is a full statement of the new idiom derived from Kulen, an idiom that was to remain the framework for all subsequent Cambodian sculpture of the Angkor period. The polished subtlety of the fleshy areas, carried on from pre-Angkor times, is here, and henceforth, modified to achieve almost abstract and architectonic ends rather than to indicate bone and joint, hence the imposing and awesome inhumanity of these early Angkor images of major Hindu deities. While this was later modified to a degree in the sensuous grace of the Baphuon style (Nos. 21, 22, 23, 26) and particularly so in the Buddhist images of the Bayon (Nos. 49, 51), the image tradition of Angkor was properly super-human and if approachable, only in the mental and physical postures of submission.

Such an appearance for these images at least

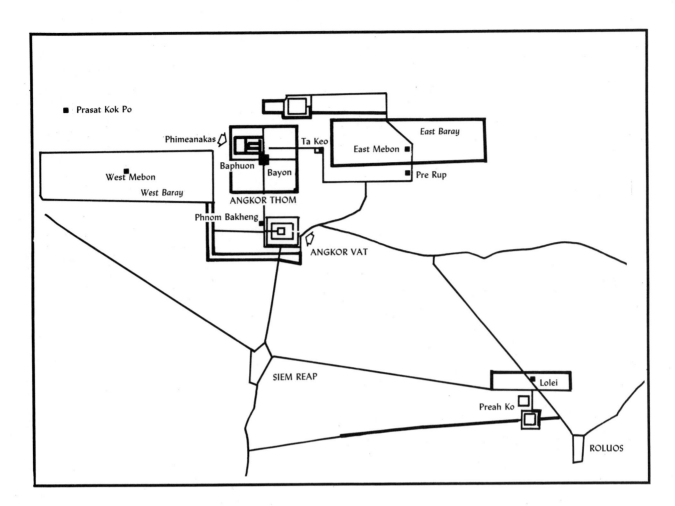

Cambodian Temple Sites

parallels, or is even implicit in, the peculiarly extreme development of the concept of the God-King (Deva-Rāja) in Cambodia. Jayavarman II certainly derived the concept from India (the "Chakravartin" or world ruler) by way of the Śrīvijaya Kingdom of Southeast Asia. But the obsessive consistency of the doctrine of the King as God on Earth, of the King as Ruler of the (World) Mountain is best symbolized by the visage of Jayavarman VII, repeated numerous times on a colossal scale in stone, looking out over the kingdom from the towers of the elevated Bayon (Fig. 8). The Cambodian theocracy carried this doctrine of the God-King to a point where it permeated the appearance of every male, human image in the round: thus the rigidly erect pose and the impassive face with its remote smile—a smile tempered by humanity only in those representations inspired by Buddhism, with its leaven of compassion which was retained even in Cambodia. And perhaps the influence of this same doctrine, whether effective in conscious terms or not, was responsible for the peculiarly Cambodian emphasis on figures in the round, emanating their magic power to the four directions.

The female figures, while following the direction of stylistic change like the males, possess a consistently more sensuous, even gracious air. In this man's world, where the divine energy of the God and God-King was represented by the repeated image of the lingam in all the major and minor temples, the place of the female as a softer and receptive complement to masculine virility permitted the sculptor the delights of delicacy and refinement, particularly in the representation of the usually nude torso. The architectonic, four-square character of the image in the round still provides boundaries beyond which the artist rarely strays (Fig. 9), and then only in the fluid medium of wax cast into bronze. Still, sensuous delight clearly comes through in many of the female figures, whether in the relatively rigid Koh Ker style (No. 12) or in the more easily adaptable works of the Baphuon phase (Nos. 19, 20). However something of male awesomeness appears in female images of the great Goddess Devi in her more powerful aspects (No. 15). The later female figures of the second Angkor phase (Nos. 41, 42, 43) follow in an accelerated way the later decorative tendencies of Cambodian art. They are usually elegant, wiry or supple, and seemingly younger sisters to the females of the first Angkor style.

Stylistically, the evolution of Angkor sculpture in the round can be seen in the admittedly incomplete sequence of sculptures in the exhibition. Following the lead of Kulen, the works from the mid-eighth to the mid-ninth century display a strong architectonic rigidity with a clear and decisive separation of parts. The block-like character of an imagined frame for the image, ultimately derived from the original rectangular block itself, is nearly always present (Nos. 10, 15, 16) and is particularly stressed in this hundred-year continuum. Linear detail is either deeply cut or indicated by the sharp edges of planes in relief; and their major directions are either vertical or horizontal, thus continuing the emphasis on the four-square, block-like effect of the images.

From about 967, a date derived from an inscription at Banteay Srei (Fig. 10) until the mid-eleventh century and the building of Angkor Vat by Sūryavarman II, a flowing softness and visual unity of the whole over the parts becomes more and more characteristic. In a sense, the closely related styles of this hundred years—Banteay Srei, Kleang and Baphuon—seem to be partly archaistic, a return to the subtle unification of the parts of the figure we have seen in the pre-Angkorean sculptures. The de-emphasis of drapery and headdress relief, the use of lightly incised or quietly indicated plane edges in the lower garments is also related to the work produced before Bakheng and Roluos, and even before Kulen. The transition to this gracious style is made at Banteay Srei (Fig. 11), unfortunately

not represented here by any single figures in relief or the round, though a lovely architectural fragment can be seen (No. 18). However, the classic expression of the new manner in the works associated with the Baphuon of Angkor is shown here by a particularly fine group of sculptures (Nos. 19–27) including similar types where the subtlety and refinement of the variations within a theme can be savored at leisure. While the careful and sensitive articulation of the human figure did not interest the sculptors of the Baphuon style, the other accomplishments of the pre-Angkor sculptors are surely echoed in the images by the later masters. One need only compare the Cleveland Vishnu of the seventh century (No. 6) with the Śiva from the Heller collection (No. 22) to see the close relationship of the two, a relationship sufficiently near and significant to warrant the use of the words archaic and archaistic respectively. Of course, the extroverted virility of the earlier figure is quite unlike the almost brooding "morbidezza" of the later one. Each has its creative place despite the derivation of the later Śiva from earlier prototypes.

The whole question of archaism in Cambodian art deserves more careful attention than it has hitherto been given.[15] The situation is particularly uncertain since the dating of these sculptures by the

[15]Bibl. 17.

26

Fig. 18   Entrance to Preah Khan temple, late twelfth–early thirteenth century.
Fig. 19   Sras Srang ghat, Banteay Kdei, late twelfth–early thirteenth century.

French scholars, the only ones with full and intimate knowledge of the field, is often dependent upon an almost Cartesian ordering of details of costume and the super-imposition of a rigid chronology upon a sequence of garment details drawn from the dated or dateable monuments. Hence the presence of numerous line drawings in the critical texts carefully delineating and defining details of girdles, belt tucks, "sampot" length, chignon interlacings, and jeweled ornaments. The resulting chronologies are impressive and surely in large part correct. Without such sequences even the primitive order obtaining in the present exhibition would have been impossible. Nevertheless, archaism seems to this writer one of the most characteristic byways of Cambodian art and when representational details disagree with general stylistic flavors one cannot ignore the latter considerations. Such tensions may, but do not necessarily, indicate forgeries—another, even more damaging problem that increasingly confronts the contemporary collector. The quality of the work, determined by mental or actual comparison, is often the deciding factor and one can accept with fervor the authority of such masterworks as the Buffalo fragment (No. 19) in providing a bench mark for the Baphuon style.

The reign of Sūryavarman II (1113–c. 1150) coincides with the style of Angkor Vat (Fig. 1),
physically the largest single ensemble in Cambodian architectural history and certainly the most famous of all Khmer monuments. Designed as a funerary monument, with its miles of galleries and its manmade terraces and towered World Mountain, Angkor Vat above all exemplifies the Cambodian penchant for architectural sculpture and decoration. The relatively few stone sculptures in the round pale by comparison with the work in relief (Fig. 5). This, added to the fame and careful protection of the famous monument, explains in part why so little aesthetically interesting sculpture of the period is to be found detached from its setting. The relief sculptures of Angkor Vat, with their typical very low carving and emphasis on detail, are the appropriate vehicles for the linearity and precision of the mid-twelfth century style.

Thus, it is no coincidence that this period is represented here only by sculpture in metal (Nos. 28–35). For these same qualities are characteristic of the bronze medium, probably cast through the lost wax process, usually with a core of sand and organic material in the larger figures. The plasticity and suppleness of the wax in the model, combined with the tense profiles and minute detail inherent in the final metal objects, made it possible to realize on a small scale the primarily linear and decorative art of the great stone reliefs. While the dating of

Cambodian bronze sculpture is much more prob-lematical than that of the stones, it is still evident that, except for the extraordinary pre-Angkor pro-ductions (No. 8), the bronzes before the period of Angkor Vat are not numerous, are generally of substantial size, and usually qualitatively inferior to their counterparts in stone. With the reign of Sūryavarman II, on the contrary, we find numerous small bronze images, often of excellent quality, as well as many metal ornamental objects—finials (No. 34), rings, hooks, etc. These find their counterparts in the Angkor Vat and later reliefs which illustrate historical or epic narratives as if they were scenes of contemporary life (Fig. 12). It is as if a decorative fashion had taken hold and flourished, as if the "horror vacui" already traditionally present in ornamental stone reliefs had spread to the accoutrements of everyday royal and noble existence—chariots, thrones, barges. The vogue, if indeed it can be accepted as one, continued into the succeeding Bayon style of the late twelfth and early thirteenth century (Nos. 56–59) and can be seen in a climactic way in the extraordinary complexity of the decorative castings on the large enthroned Buddha of the thirteenth century (No. 61).

The bronze images themselves were probably private objects of devotion, though one must recognize that even these would have been accessible only to persons of noble or royal rank. In consider-ing their merits one is constantly forced away from the faces towards the surrounding decorative detail. The small almond eyes, so characteristic of the period of Angkor Vat, and the, by now, quite dutiful smile, are set amidst a variety of floral and drapery development more readily compliant to the decorative interests of the artist. The skirt of the female deity (No. 32), the "torana" and crowning tree of the meditating Buddha (No. 30), or the spreading Naga hood of the cult image (Nos. 28, 29) are the sculptural images we remember and which were, judging by the care and inspiration embodied in their creation, the primary concern of the artist. Perhaps the most striking correlation of the quality of the bronzes with that of the finest sculptures of Angkor Vat, the reliefs of the grand gallery, is a comparison of the Detroit bronze Garuda (No. 33) with its mate in stone relief, the Garuda bearing Krishna.[16]

The coronation of Jayavarman VII in 1181 brought to the Cambodian throne its last and in some ways most remarkable king. But four years before, the Chams, from present day Viet-Nam, had razed Angkor. The new king succeeded in expelling the invaders and then embarked on an unprecedented series of architectural undertakings, culminating in

[16] Bibl. 25, fig. 120.

30

the erection of the Bayon about or just after 1190. Jayavarman VII elevated Buddhism, hitherto subservient to Śaivite and Vaishnavite Hinduism, to a dominant position, in a syncretic religion encompassing both faiths. Contemporary inscriptions testify to a broadening of the base for faith and good works. The compassionate ideal of Buddhism was made manifest, at least partially, in royal favors and was reflected in the aesthetic and representational flavor of the sculptures on the monuments.

While the colossal masks of the God-King (Lokeśvara-Jayavarman) on the Towers of the Bayon (Fig. 8) are perforce more rigidly architectural and schematic than their smaller counterparts on the images (No. 50), they demonstrate on a broad scale the essentials of the last major style of Khmer sculpture. These are the thick lips set in a mysterious, brooding smile, the wide, flattened nostrils of an ample nose, and the slitted downcast eyes—the whole reflecting a memory of sensuousness tempered by the compassion of a Bodhisattva. The scale and positioning of the masks on the Bayon Towers still attest the continuing concept of the world ruler contemplating the distant reaches of his empire; the gaze, however, does not reach out but turns in, as if awaiting the termination of royal power.

These facial characteristics and the psychological tone of the Bayon masks permeate nearly all of the images of Buddhas and Bodhisattvas (Nos. 47–54), the most common of the latter being Lokeśvara, "the lord of all the worlds." If we can accept the usual identification of the famous stone image at Phnom Penh[17] as a portrait of Jayavarman VII, then the physiognomy of this man established the facial type of images in the Bayon style. If not, then the style so permeated the images of the day as to become the only way to see the royal presence. In either case the assumed appearance of the Deva-Rāja fulfilled all the needs of the representational art of the time. And it is an unforgettable, archetypal image now accepted as the symbol of Cambodian art, affecting all of the production of Angkor by the power of its smiling presence.

This concentration on the face is characteristic of the last phase of the art of Angkor. The sheer mass of work that was produced precluded attention to all detail. The usual criticisms of Bayon work as hasty and particularly uneven is surely just. Bodies and drapery details are summarily executed, though general effects of liveliness and animation are still achieved by the most gifted artists (Nos. 40–42). In some of the subsidiary figures of demons, ascetics ("rishis") (No. 44), or animals (No. 45), vigorous and individual handling can come forth.

---

[17] Bibl. 24, pp. 97, 109.

31

Fig. 20   Devata, Angkor Vat relief, twelfth century.

The colossal heads of the demons lining the causeway approaches to Angkor Thom (Fig. 13) are particularly interesting for the individuality of their faces, and in the sculptor's evident concern for muscular detail. The resemblance to Chinese guardian types from the T'ang dynasty onwards is surely more than coincidental. But the stereotyped bodies attached to the well-differentiated heads only emphasize the primary interest of the Bayon artists in facial expressiveness.

The period after the death of Jayavarman VII in 1219 was certainly not barren, for occasional works of great quality continued to be made, especially in bronze. The large and accomplished crowned Buddha of the Kimbell Foundation is an isolated and remarkable example. Works in wood and stone, continuations of unfinished work at Angkor Thom and the Bayon, were produced, but without innovation or conviction. Much of the sculpture of the Bayon, especially that in relief, even seems to fall into the condition of folk production. The last syncretic effort in religion under Jayavarman VII and the enormous physical tasks required by the God-King could well have sapped the creative energy of any people. The later art of Cambodia rests in the condition of folk art the world over—a simplified and relaxed but hazy and troubled memory image of a stirring past.

Chronology

ARCHAIC PERIOD: 3rd century A.D.–mid 6th century A.D.; Funan Empire.

Kings	Historical events & Capitals	Artistic Styles*
PRE-ANGKOREAN PERIOD		
550–600 Bhavavarman I	capital unknown—vicinity of Vat Phu	540–600 Phnom Da
600–616 Mahendravarman		600–650 Sambor Prei Kuk
616–635 Iśanavarman I		
635–656 Bhavavarman II	Angkor Borei—capital	635–700 Prei Kmeng
656–681 Jayavarman I		
	Division of Chenla and	700–750 Prasat Andet
	Javanese Raids	706–800 Kompong Preah
TRANSITIONAL PERIOD		
802–850 Jayavarman II	Indrapura & Phnom Kulen	825–875 Phnom Kulen
	(Mt. Mahendra)—capitals	
850–877 Jayavarman III	Roluos (Hariharālaya)—capital	*Kok Po 857*
ANGKOREAN PERIOD		
877–889 Indravarman I	Roluos—capital	875–893 Preah Ko
889–900 Yaśovarman I	Roluos & Yaśodharapura (Angkor)—capitals	893–925 Bakheng
		Lolei 893
900– Harshavarman I		
–921 Iśanavarman II		
921–941 Jayavarman IV	Koh Ker—capital	921†–945 Koh Ker
941–944 Harshavarman II		
944–968 Rajendravarman	Angkor becomes capital from now on	947–965 Pre Rup
		Eastern Mebon 947, Pre Rup 961
968–1001 Jayavarman V		967†–1000 Banteay Srei
		965–1010 Khleang
1001–1002 Udayādityavarman I		*Ta Keo, Phimeanakas*
1002–1050 Sūryavarman	1003–1011 War of Succession	1010–1080 Baphuon
1050–1066 Udayādityavarman II		*Western Mebon, Vat Phu*
1066–1080 Harshavarman III		
1080–1107 Jayavarman VI		
1107–1113 Dharanīndravarman I		1100–1175 Angkor Vat
1113–1150 Sūryavarman II	civil war	*Thommanon, Banteay*
1150–1160 Dharanīndravarman II	1145–Khmers invade Champa	*Samre, Chausay Tevoda,*
1160–1165 Yaśovarman II		*Beng Mealea*
1165–1177 Tribhuvanādityavarman		
	1177–Cham invasion	1177–1230 Bayon (Angkor Thom)
1181–1219 Jayavarman VII	1203–Champa becomes Khmer province	*Banteay Kdei, Preah Khan 1191,*
1220–1243 Indravarman II	1120–Evacuation of Champa	*Neak Pean, Banteay Chmar,*
1243–1295 Jayavarman VIII	1282–Mongol threats	*Royal Terraces*
1295–1307 Srīndravarman		
1307–1327 Srīndrajayavarman		
1327– Jayavarmadiparameśvara		
	1353–Angkor seized by the Thai	
	1431–Recapture of Angkor by the Thai	
	Phnom Penh–capital	

*The dates of the artistic styles are after Bibl. 7, p. 42. All of the dates are approximate except those marked†, which are from inscriptions. Names of monuments are set in italics.

Plates

1   Bust of Sūrya. Style of Śrī Deb, sixth–seventh century. Sandstone; H. 22 in.

1   Bust of Sūrya.

3 Head of Buddha. Probably from Angkor Borei, seventh century. Gray sandstone; H. 10 in.

2 Head of a Female. Sixth–seventh century. Green sandstone; H. 9¾ in.

4   Male figure. Style of Phnom Da or Sambor Prei Kuk, sixth–seventh century. Stone; H. 13¾ in.

5 Female Torso. Style of Sambor Prei Kuk or Prei Kmeng, seventh century. Stone; H. 7⅞ in.

6   Vishnu. Style of Prasat Andet, second half of the seventh century. Sandstone; H. 34¼ in.

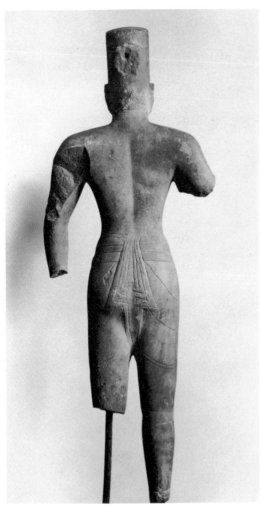

6   Back view.

7   Vishnu. Style of Prasat Andet, second half of the seventh
century. Sandstone; H. 19⅝ in.

8   Maitreya from Pra Kon Chai. Probably style of Kompong Preah, eighth century. Bronze; H. 38½ in.

10 Brahmā. Style of Bakheng, reportedly from Prasat Prei, late ninth–early tenth century. Limestone; H. 47½ in.

11 Head of Śiva. Style of Koh Ker, second quarter of the tenth century. Sandstone; H. 16½ in.

10 Back view.

12 Female Divinity. Style of Koh Ker, second quarter of the tenth century.
Stone; H. 35 13/16 in.

13 Rākshasa. Style of Koh Ker, second quarter
of the tenth century. Sandstone; H. 27½ in.
Front and back views.

14 Four-armed Standing Rākshasa. Style of Koh Ker,
second quarter of the tenth century. Bronze;
H. 6 11/16 in.

15 Devī in Her Aspect as Durgā. Style of Koh Ker, second quarter of the
tenth century. Bronze; H. 17 3/4 in.

16   Four-armed Vishnu. Style of Pre Rup, mid-tenth century. Polished sandstone; H. 56 in.

17   Head of Śiva. Style of Pre Rup, mid-tenth century. Stone; H. 13 in.

18   Part of a Lintel with Indra on the Three-headed Elephant Airavata. Style of Banteay Srei,
second half of the tenth century. Reddish sandstone; H. 22½ in., W. 16¼ in.

19   Female Torso. First quarter of the eleventh century. Dark gray sandstone; H. 15½ in.

20   Female Figure. First quarter of the eleventh century. Grayish-green stone; H. 38¾ in.

21 Śiva. First half of the eleventh century. Gray sandstone; H. 30¼ in.

22 Śiva. First half of the eleventh century. Stone; H. 53 in.

22   Back view.

23   Standing Male Figure.
First half of the eleventh century.
Buff sandstone; H. 28½ in.

24 Head of Brahmanical Deity. First half of the eleventh century. Sandstone; H. $9\frac{5}{16}$ in.

25 Head of Buddha. First half of the eleventh century. Dark stone; H. 9⅝ in.

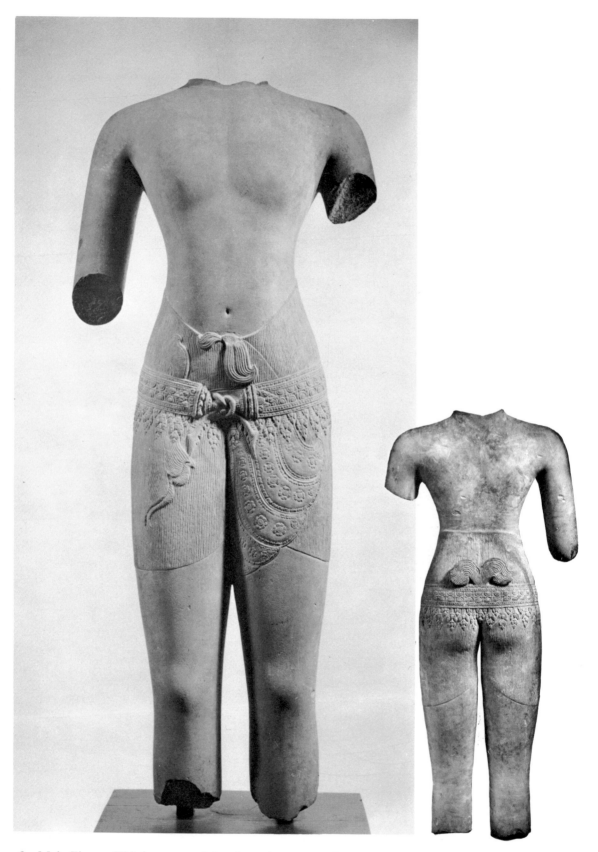

26   Male Figure. Third quarter of the eleventh century. Green sandstone; H. 52½ in. *Front and back views.*

27 Female Figure. Third quarter of the eleventh century. Sandstone; H. 36 in.

28 Perhaps Bhaisajyaguru (Buddha of Healing).
First half of the twelfth century. Bronze; H. 23 in.
Front and back views.

29 Buddha Sheltered by Mucalinda. First half of the twelfth century. Bronze; H. 16½ in.

30 Buddha Enthroned. First half of the twelfth century. Bronze; H. 10½ in.

32 Four-armed Female Divinity.
First half of the twelfth century. Bronze; H. 8 3/16 in.

31 Vajrasattva. Back view. *See p. 71.*

31 Vajrasattva. First half of the twelfth century. Bronze; H. 5 in.

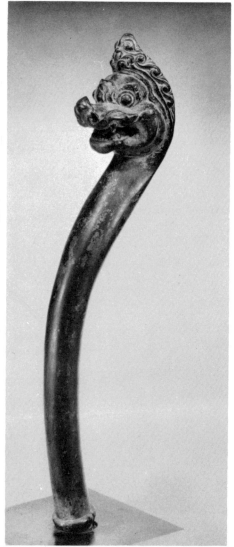

33   Garuda. First half of the twelfth century.
Bronze; H. 9¾ in.

34   Metal Finial. First half of the twelfth century. Bronze; H. 20⅞ in.

35   Vishnu on Garuda. Second half of the twelfth century. Gilt bronze; H. 6⅝ in.

36   Jambhala. Second half of the twelfth century. Bronze; H. 8⅛ in.

37 Conch. Second half of the twelfth century. Bronze; H. 10½ in.

38   Lakshmi (?). Late twelfth century. Bronze; H. 9¼ in.

39 Standing Vishnu. Late twelfth century. Bronze; H. $9\frac{1}{16}$ in.

40   Part of a Lintel with Rāmāyana Scene. Late twelfth century. Red sandstone; H. 35 in., W. 74 in.

41   Frieze with Apsaras. Late twelfth–early thirteenth century. Sandstone; H. 10 in., W. 34½ in.

42   Fragment of a Pillar with Dancing Apsaras. Late twelfth–early
thirteenth century. Limestone; H. 33 in., W. 16½ in.

43 Relief of Apsara. Probably from the Terrace of the Leper King,
late twelfth–early thirteenth century. Sandstone; H. 24 in., W. 13 in.

44   Figure of a Hermit. Late twelfth–early thirteenth century. Stone; H. 20 in.

45   Guardian Lion. Late twelfth–early thirteenth century. Sandstone; H. 29½ in. *Front and side views.*

46   Head of Buddha. Late twelfth–early thirteenth century. Sandstone; H. 13½ in.

48 Fragment of a Head. Late twelfth–early
thirteenth century. Stone; H. 9½ in.

47 Head of Buddha. Late twelfth–early thirteenth century. Stone; H. 8½ in.

49   Bust of Buddha with Naga Hood. Reportedly from Chausay Temple,
late twelfth–early thirteenth century. Limestone; H. 35 in.

50   Head of Lokeśvara. Late twelfth–early thirteenth
century. Pink sandstone; H. 13⅞ in.

52   Head of Prājñāparamitā. Late twelfth–early
thirteenth century. Sandstone; H. 14 9/16 in.

51 Bust of the Eleven-headed Avalokiteśvara. From Porte des Mortes,
late twelfth–early thirteenth century. Grayish limestone; H. 52 in.

51   Side view.

53(a)   Royal Couple: King. Late twelfth–early thirteenth century.
Sandstone; H. 54 in.

53(b)   Queen. H. 55 in.

54 Buddha Sheltered by Mucalinda, Bhaisajyaguru (?).
Late twelfth–early thirteenth century. Bronze; H. 11½ in.

55 Vajrasattva. Twelfth–thirteenth century. Bronze; H. 7¼ in.

56 Finial with the Temptation of Buddha by Māra. Late twelfth–early
thirteenth century. Bronze; H. $15\frac{7}{16}$ in.

59 Garuda Finial. Late twelfth–early thirteenth century. Bronze; H. $9\frac{1}{4}$ in.

58 Palanquin Hook and Ring. Late twelfth–early thirteenth century. Bronze; (hook) H. $8\frac{5}{8}$ in., W. $3\frac{1}{4}$ in.; (ring) H. $6\frac{5}{8}$ in., W. 7 in.

57   Garuda Terminal. Late twelfth–early thirteenth century. Bronze; H. 7$\frac{1}{8}$ in.

60 Pillar with Apsara. Thirteenth century. Reddish sandstone; H. 30¾ in., W. 13 in.

61   Buddha Enthroned. Thirteenth–early fourteenth century. Bronze; H. 68⅛ in., W. 27¼ in.

Catalogue

1   BUST OF SŪRYA
    Pre-Angkorean Period, style of Śrī Deb, sixth–seventh century
    Sandstone; H. 22 in.

In Śrī Deb, situated in what is now central Siam, a separate school of sculpture was formed which remained under the strong inspiration of Indian sculpture. The political affiliation of Śrī Deb to the Funan, Chenla, or Dvaravati empires is not yet satisfactorily determined, although there is a good possibility that it may have been one of the most northern sites of the Funan Empire, formed by a group of rather autonomous states (Bibl. 22, p. 240. See also Bibl. 9, p. 30). There is also the problem of the relationship of this culture to that of the Śrīvijaya Empire of Southeast Asia, based on Sumatra and Java but extending into what became southern Cambodia and Siam. The sculpture of Śrī Deb is Vaishnavite, in contrast to Buddhist Dvaravati sculpture, which seems to connect it closer with the Hindu-directed Funan art (Bibl. 9, p. 31).

The god wears a high crown of the *kirīta-makuṭa* type, with his hair coming from beneath the crown and falling in locks on his shoulders. The huge earrings and broken halo indicate that the figure is meant to represent the sun god, Sūrya. This previously unpublished bust is surely one of the most individual and beautiful remains from early Southeast Asia.

Cf. Bibl. 22, p. 262.

Collection of Mr. and Mrs. Ben Heller, New York.

2   HEAD OF A FEMALE
    Pre-Angkorean Period, sixth–seventh century
    Green sandstone; H. 9⅜ in.

This female head is not too far from the style which is represented by the head of Sūrya (No. 1). It has the same recessed, almond-shaped eyes, naturally arched eyebrows, small nose, and sensitively cut mouth. She has small ears, without exaggeratedly long ear lobes, in which discreet earrings are placed. The hair is pulled back and supported by a band, with its ends placed under the band and falling in natural locks at the sides and back of the head. There is nothing quite comparable to this head in Cambodian art, but the closest comparisons are with some of the female sculptures dating to the seventh century (Bibl. 24, p. 204, cat. 10, and p. 59, pl. 16). There is the perfection of a classical masterpiece in this sculpture, in the depiction of the beautiful physical type as well as in the unusually careful execution. The right side of the head is badly damaged.

Collection of Mr. Peter Marks, New York.

3   HEAD OF BUDDHA
    Pre-Angkorean Period, probably from Angkor Borei, seventh
      century
    Gray sandstone; H. 10 in.

The head probably belongs to the school of sculpture from Angkor Borei, which was a center of Buddhist art during the seventh century. The Buddha has snail-like, curly hair, long ear lobes, and a rather broad face with a slightly hooked nose, narrow, long, downcast eyes, and a wide mouth with the trace of what is to become a smile. All of these characteristics, derived from the classic Gupta Buddha images of India, are common to Angkor Borei sculptures.

Cf. Bibl. 24, pls. 6–9, pp. 39–44.

Publ. and Exh.: Howard C. Hollis, "A Khmer Head," *Bulletin of The Cleveland Museum of Art*, vol. XIX (December 1932), pp. 163–165, illus. p. 161; *Art Digest* (December 15, 1932), p. 17; *American Magazine of Art*, vol. XXVI (January 1933), p. 50; *Bulletin of The Cleveland Museum of Art*, vol. XXVIII (June 1941), illus. p. 100; *Buddhist Art* (exhibition, Detroit: Detroit Institute of Arts, October 1942), No. 29, p. 49; *Liturgical Arts* (February 1946), pp. 37–40; *Handbook of The Cleveland Museum of Art* (1958), No. 785; Margaret F. Marcus, "Buddha Sheltered by Mucalinda," *Bulletin of The Cleveland Museum of Art*, vol. LII (September 1965), p. 192, illus.; *Handbook of The Cleveland Museum of Art* (1966), p. 241.

The Cleveland Museum of Art; Dudley P. Allen Fund.

4   MALE FIGURE
    Pre-Angkorean Period, style of Phnom Da or Sambor Prei
      Kuk, sixth–seventh century
    Stone; H. 13¾ in.

The way in which the garment worn by the figure is pleated in front and held on the hips by a twisted scarf gives a clue to an early dating. This arrangement of the draperies is common in Phnom Da style (Bibl. 4, p. 69, pl. XV, 1; Bibl. 24, p. 208, cat. 22 [same in Bibl. 20, pl. XVII-A]) and it continues into the following Sambor style (Bibl. 24, p. 202, cat. 4, text p. 44). It is interesting to notice that this heavily accentuated pleating of the skirt in some of the early Cambodian sculptures had a practical function, serving as a support for the figure (Bibl. 20, pls. 1B, XVIII). It may also be seen as the proto-image for the "fish-tail" or "anchor" girdle of later times.

The Denver Art Museum.

5 FEMALE TORSO
Pre-Angkorean Period, style of Sambor Prei Kuk or Prei
    Kmeng, seventh century
Stone; H. 7⅞ in.

The female torso has full, highly placed breasts and a narrow
waist. The folds under the breasts are characteristic of the style
of Sambor Prei Kuk (Bibl. 20, p. 176), and still continue to appear in some of the female figures of the Prasat Andet style
(Bibl. 20, pl. XXXVII-B). Later on these folds are replaced by incised lines (No. 12). The triple folds around the neck (*kambugrīva*)
appear quite rarely in Cambodian sculpture and are an unusual
feature. The projecting nipples are also characteristic of the
Sambor Prei Kuk style (Bibl. 24, p. 51, pl. 13, and p. 53, pl. 14).

Collection of Mr. Georges Halphen, La Chapelle en Serval (Oise).

6 VISHNU
Pre-Angkorean Period, style of Prasat Andet, second half of
    the seventh century
Sandstone; H. 34¼ in.

Originally the figure had four arms, with each hand holding one
of Vishnu's attributes. It was attached to a supporting arch,
part of which still can be traced on the back of the head. The god
wears a short garment (*sampot*) tied in such a way that it forms a
loop on the left side. One of the extreme ends of the cloth hangs
free on the right side, and the other is drawn between the legs and
attached at the back. This arrangement of the *sampot*, forming a
loop on the left side of the figure is one of the characteristic
features of the Prasat Andet style, although it appears also in
Prei Kmeng style. In earlier styles—Phnom Da and Sambor—the
loop was placed in the center. The hip belt, usually supporting
the *sampot*, is replaced here by a scarf tied around the hips. Among
other peculiarities of the Prasat Andet style is the special shape of
the cylindrical cap (*kirīta-makuṭa*) which descends very low on the
neck and encircles the ear, forming a point on the temple. The
ears have very short ear lobes. The face is round, with eyes of a
new shape, more perfected, and with a narrow tear channel and a
double-wave line on the lower lid. The face wears a half smiling
expression, indicative of the later mysterious smile so typical of
Cambodian art. The muscular torso of the god reflects the influence of some earlier Vishnu sculptures (Bibl. 20, pl. XVII-B)
and is not too far removed from the Indian prototypes.

Publ. and Exh.: Hollis, "Two Pre-Khmer Statues of Vishnu,"
Bulletin of The Cleveland Museum of Art, XXIX (December 1942),
pp. 164–166, illus. p. 161; *The Art of Greater India* (exhibition, Los
Angeles: Los Angeles County Museum of Art, 1950), No. 147;
Bibl. 20, pp. 166 ff., pl. XXXIII-B; *Handbook of The Cleveland
Museum of Art* (1958), No. 786; *Khmer Sculpture* (exhibition, New
York: Asia House Gallery, November 28, 1961–January 28, 1962),
No. 2(K), illus. p. 19; *Art News* (December 1961), illus. p. 43;
Sherman E. Lee, *A History of Far Eastern Art*, New York, 1964,
p. 228, fig. 286; *Handbook of The Cleveland Museum of Art* (1966),
p. 241; *Selected Works: The Cleveland Museum of Art* (1967), pl. 45.

The Cleveland Museum of Art; Purchase, Leonard C. Hanna, Jr.
Bequest.

7 VISHNU
Pre-Angkorean Period, style of Prasat Andet, second half of
    the seventh century
Sandstone; H. 19⅝ in.

The sculpture relates closely to the other figure of Vishnu from
Cleveland (No. 6). Originally it had four arms, like No. 6,
although there is no indication of a supporting halo (contrary to
the opinion expressed by Dupont in Bibl. 20, p. 171). In details
such as the cylindrical cap, which closely follows the contour of
the ears and descends low on the neck, the short ear lobes, the
shape of the eyes, and the round face with the slight smile, as well
as the *sampot* associated with the hip scarf, the statue is related
closely to No. 6. New are the appearance of the moustache and a
different treatment of the torso, which is much less muscular than
that of No. 6. This treatment of the torso is related to later
traditions.

Publ.: Hollis, "Two Pre-Khmer Statues of Vishnu," illus.
p. 171; Bibl. 20, pp. 166 ff., pl. XXXIV-B.

The Cleveland Museum of Art; Purchase, Leonard C. Hanna, Jr.
Bequest.

8 MAITREYA FROM PRA KON CHAI
Pre-Angkorean Period, probably style of Kompong Preah,
    eighth century
Bronze; H. 38½ in.

This superb Maitreya is represented as a youthful male with
slender body dressed in a very short *sampot*. The high chignon,
braided in loops, contains in its center a small stupa which gives a
clue to the iconography of the figure. The figure has four arms,
and the hands, with long tapering fingers, express a gesture
similar to the *vitarka mudrā*. It is possible, however, that they might
have carried various detachable attributes (Bibl. 24, p. 129). The
face has a high forehead, straight nose, full lips, a moustache, and
downcast, silver-inlaid eyes with pupils of another metal. The
features are modeled with unusual care and delicacy.

There are a number of pre-Angkorean bronzes of this type
which date to the period between Pre Kmeng and Kompong
Preah (Bibl. 8, pp. 275–334). They vary slightly in style and all
reflect a high technical skill and sophistication. The technique in
which they were done was a *cire perdue* process using a core of
clay with aggregate, and the metal used was most frequently
bronze with a high content of copper. Often, more precious metals
such as silver and gold were added to this alloy. This type of metal,
most favored by Cambodians, was known as *samrit*. The surface
of the bronze was also frequently gilded, though not in this case.

The iconography of almost all pre-Angkorean bronzes is
Buddhist. (An exception is the bronze representing Śiva and Uma
on a bull, Nandi. This however, was probably a copy after an
Indian image [Bibl. 24, p. 123].) Maitreya, frequently represented
in bronze, is scarcely, if at all, found in the stone sculpture.

Cf. Bibl. 4, pl. 104; Bibl. 20, pls. 29, 30.

Publ.: Bibl. 8, fig. 23.

Collection of Mr. and Mrs. John D. Rockefeller 3rd, New York.

9 LINTEL WITH GARUDA
   Style of Preah Ko, perhaps from Kok Po, Prasat D, late
      ninth century
   Sandstone; H. 20 $\frac{11}{16}$ in., W. 46$\frac{1}{2}$ in.

The relief is part of a door lintel, decorated in the center with a Garuda figure holding the extremes of two snake-garlands which end in three-headed hoods. The surrounding space is filled, in the usual manner, with stylized vegetal decor. This symmetrical arrangement, with Garuda in the center and flanked by multi-headed snakes, is characteristic of the Preah Ko style (Bibl. 40, pls. XLVII-C, XLVIII-B, C). This sculpture is closest to the lintels of Prasat D of Kok Po (*Ibid.*, pl. XLVIII-A). Although the main temple of Kok Po dates to 857 A.D., it contains buildings of various periods (*Ibid.*, p. 145). Prasat D (to which we think this lintel belongs) dates probably to 883 A.D. This is indicated by the inscription (Bibl. 12, p. 379) which mentions a construction of two prasats, the second one (erected in 883 A.D.) probably being Prasat D.

Publ.: Bulletin of The Cleveland Museum of Art, vol. LIV (December 1967), p. 347, No. 170, illus. p. 332; Margaret F. Marcus, "A Cambodian Sculptured Lintel," *Bulletin of The Cleveland Museum of Art*, vol. LV (December 1968), pp. 321–330, illus.

The Cleveland Museum of Art; John L. Severance Fund.

10 BRAHMĀ
   Style of Bakheng, reportedly from Prasat Prei, late ninth–
      early tenth century
   Limestone; H. 47$\frac{1}{2}$ in.

This four-headed, four-armed figure of Brahmā is reportedly from Prasat Prei. That temple, however, belongs to the reign of Jayavarman II (first half of the ninth century), whereas the style to which the sculpture belongs is a pure Bakheng style. Therefore, if the information that it comes from Prasat Prei is correct, it must belong to a later phase of this building.

Brahmā wears a *sampot* with the loop on the left side and a pleated, double anchor or fish-tail pendant supported by a belt. The manner in which this garment is arranged is typical of the Bakheng style (Bibl. 7, p. 247, fig. 58-c). Also typical of this period is a certain rigidity and stiffness of the figure.

Cf. Bibl. 7, pl. XXXIV, 2; Bibl. 4, pl. 38.

Publ.: Bulletin of The Metropolitan Museum of Art, vol. XXXII, No. 4 (April 1937), p. 88, fig. 5.

The Metropolitan Museum of Art, New York; Fletcher Fund, 1935.

11 HEAD OF ŚIVA
   Style of Koh Ker, second quarter of the tenth century
   Sandstone; H. 16$\frac{1}{2}$ in.

The third eye lightly incised on the forehead indicates that the deity is Śiva. The hairdress (*jaṭā-makuṭa*) is of a type that could be worn by an ordinary mortal of a high social rank. This, however, is not surprising in view of the now fully developed Cambodian religious concept, the cult of the Deva-Rāja (God-King). This belief, deriving directly from the Hindu worship of the *chakravartin*, gained great popularity in Cambodian art especially during the Angkorean Period.

The treatment of the head is typical of the Koh Ker style. The double-outlined lips and eyes and the strong, projecting arches of the eyebrows all take on a distinctive, native Cambodian aspect. The stone is polished and very smooth in those parts which represent the skin. The very delicate patterns of the headdress and the moustache do not break the surface of the stone, nor detract from the architectonic effect.

Publ. and Exh.: Hollis, "A Cambodian Head," *Bulletin of The Cleveland Museum of Art*, vol. XXVIII (January 1941), pp. 4, 5, illus. p. 1; *Museum Journal* (April 1941), p. 17; *Liturgical Arts* (February 1946), pp. 37–40; *Handbook of The Cleveland Museum of Art* (1958), No. 787; *The Cleveland Museum of Art*, New York, 1958, p. 16; *Khmer Sculpture* (New York), No. 7 (K), illus. pp. 24, 25; *Pantheon* (January–February 1962), illus. p. 54; Christopher Pym, "Angkor," *Enigmatic Cultures*, Edward Bacon, ed., London, 1962, illus.; Lee, *A History of Far Eastern Art*, p. 233, fig. 296; *Handbook of The Cleveland Museum of Art* (1966), p. 241; *Selected Works: The Cleveland Museum of Art*, pl. 46.

The Cleveland Museum of Art; Purchase from the J. H. Wade Fund.

12 FEMALE DIVINITY
   Style of Koh Ker, second quarter of the tenth century
   Stone; H. 35$\frac{13}{16}$ in.

Judging from the remaining fragments of the arms, the figure was once four-armed and therefore meant to represent a deity. She has high, firm breasts, a narrow waist, and well-rounded hips. Under the breasts are incised lines, folds of the skin, suggesting the fleshy texture of the torso. The abdomen is marked by a deeply carved navel. The *sarong* that she wears is of a simple Koh Ker type, narrowly pleated with the round fold overhanging in the front (Bibl. 4, p. 69, pl. XV, 6, and pl. 43, A and B). Almost the same type of *sarong* reappears later in the Angkor Vat period. There, however, it differs slightly in that it has a rectangular panel with a pointed end at the front of the *sarong* (*Ibid.*, pl. 64, A and B). The figure is of exceptionally fine quality and does not give the impression of stiffness often characteristic of the Koh Ker sculpture.

Cf. Bibl. 24, p. 202, Cat. 6.

Collection of Mr. Robert Rousset, Paris.

13 RĀKSHASA
   Style of Koh Ker, second quarter of the tenth century
   Sandstone; H. 27$\frac{1}{2}$ in.

The figure represents a sturdy demon with bulging eyes and long curly hair. The legs and arms are partially broken, but there is enough left to allow speculation on the original position of the figure. It seems that the sculpture may have been one of a pair of fighting figures which were so popular during the Koh Ker Period, like those of Sugrīva and Vālin in the Musée Albert Sarraut (Bibl. 4, pls. 46, 47). In support of this theory is the fact that the front side of the demon's *sampot* is not pleated. Had the figure been interlocked in an embrace with his enemy, this part, forming the interior of the pair, could not have been worked in detail. The general feeling of tension in the body and the wind-blown hair seem to provide further evidence that the rākshasa was involved in action and was more than just the usual static type of guardian figure.

Publ.: Bulletin of The Cleveland Museum of Art, vol. LIV (December 1967), No. 176, illus. p. 333.

The Cleveland Museum of Art; John L. Severance Fund.

14 FOUR-ARMED STANDING RĀKSHASA
    Style of Koh Ker, second quarter of the tenth century
    Bronze; H. 6 $\frac{11}{16}$ in.

The face with bulging eyes suggests that the figure represents a demon (rākshasa), as does the stone figure from the Cleveland Museum of Art (No. 13). The demon's hands are in what appears to be a *vitarka mudrā*, a gesture of explanation and exposition. This gesture, very frequent with Cambodian metal figures, also may have been used to insert detachable attributes into the deity's hands (See No. 8 and E. Dale Saunders, *Mudrā*, New York, 1960, pp. 66–75).

The clothing, the crown, and the *sampot* are of Koh Ker type. We may add that, although the loop of the *sampot* disappears in the majority of Koh Ker male figures (Bibl. 24, p. 76), it is preserved in some sculptures which continued the Bakheng tradition (Bibl. 4, p. 40). There are other characteristics of the *sampot*, besides the loop, that are strongly Koh Ker. These are the semi-circular fold of the upper border of the *sampot* and the double, anchor-like pendant, shorter than the *sampot* itself, with the upper "anchor" shorter than the lower one. Finally, the leg border of the *sampot* ends in a straight horizontal line unlike the later Banteay Srei style where it takes on a diagonal form.

The George P. Bickford Collection, Cleveland.

15 DEVĪ IN HER ASPECT AS DURGĀ
    Style of Koh Ker, second quarter of the tenth century
    Bronze; H. 17 $\frac{3}{4}$ in.

The Goddess Beyond Reach, Durgā, is a terrible form of Devī in her aspect as a killer of the buffalo demon, Mahisha. The head of Mahisha can be seen at the goddess' feet. She holds in her four hands attributes of Vishnu; in the two upper hands the wheel (*chakra*) and the conch (*sankha*), and in the two lower hands the lotus bud (*padma*) and the mace (*gadā*).

It may seem somewhat surprising that the goddess carried attributes of Vishnu instead of her own, but we may speculate that the artist intended to represent her as the *sakti*, or female energy, of Vishnu. Cambodian iconography is often mixed and not quite clear. The presence of Mahisha's head emphasizes the fact that the ultimate representation intended was that of the Devī in her terrible aspect as Durgā. The artistic treatment of the bronze clearly recalls that of the stone sculpture (No. 12). It has the same full breasts, large hips, narrow waistline, and the same simply pleated *sarong*. It may be due to the difference of material, or possibly because this figure is perfectly complete, that it seems much stiffer than the stone sculpture. Were the stone figure intact, as this one is, it might, ironically enough, also appear less supple and perfect.

Publ.: Khmer Sculpture (New York), No. 3(K), p. 20.

Collection of Dr. and Mrs. Samuel Eilenberg, New York.

16 FOUR-ARMED VISHNU
    Style of Pre Rup, mid-tenth century
    Polished sandstone; H. 56 in.

The art of Pre Rup is not progressive since it continues, to some extent, the style of Koh Ker, and shows archaizing tendencies in the style of Bakheng. In fact the difference between the style of Bakheng and that of Pre Rup is sometimes difficult to determine. In this case the type of *sampot* helps in making the distinction. It is almost like that of Bakheng with the difference, however, that the upper part of the fish-tail pendant (now partially broken) is shorter than the lower one while it was vice versa in the Bakheng style (Bibl. 4, p. 43, pl. VII, 1, and p. 39, pl. VI, 1). Also, the crown worn by Vishnu is of a Pre Rup design (*Ibid.*, p. 111, pl. XXIII, 2). The high polish of the stone in areas that depict skin should be noted.

The deity represents Vishnu with four arms. The two lower hands are intact; the left one holds a lotus bud while the right one was resting on a mace, now broken. The upper arms, with hands now missing, presumably held the other attributes of Vishnu, a disk and a conch.

Publ.: James Cahill, "Oriental Art Studies and the Brundage Collection," *The Asia Foundation Program Bulletin* (No. 40, 1966), fig. 12.

Center of Asian Art and Culture, City and County of San Francisco; Avery Brundage Collection.

17 HEAD OF ŚIVA
    Style of Pre Rup, mid-tenth century
    Stone; H. 13 in.

The head is that of Śiva, as is suggested by the lightly incised third eye on the forehead and by the very unusual headgear. Besides the usual crown, much like that of the Pre Rup Vishnu (No. 16), it has a knot of braided hair on the top, decorated with the head of a snake in front (a symbol of Śiva), and hanging in the form of a pony tail in the back.

The facial features are exactly like those of the Vishnu mentioned above (No. 16). The skin is highly polished, the eyebrows form a horizontal line, and the eyes are incised in a double line. Śiva wears a moustache, and a beard which forms a point on the chin. The ears have long, pierced ear lobes. There is a faint indication of the later Angkorean smile.

Anonymous Loan.

18 PART OF A LINTEL WITH INDRA ON THE
    THREE-HEADED ELEPHANT AIRAVATA
    Style of Banteay Srei, second half of the tenth century
    Reddish sandstone; H. 22 $\frac{1}{2}$ in., W. 16 $\frac{1}{4}$ in.

The relief, representing Indra on his *vāhana* Airavata among thick foliage, is a central part of what was once a door lintel. The representations of Indra as the central motif of door lintels seem to have been particularly in vogue during the Pre Rup style, as illustrated by Fig. 14. It will be found, however, in sculpture both earlier and later than Pre Rup and it is not rare in the Banteay Srei school (Fig. 10).

The nervous way in which the foliage is treated, the pointed form of the arch which encircles Indra, as well as the treatment of the animal and the god himself persuade us that the lintel belongs to the Banteay Srei style.

Cf. Bibl. 24, p. 240, cat. 120.

Publ. and Exh.: Art in Asia and the West (exhibition, San Francisco: San Francisco Museum of Art, October 28–December 1, 1957), No. 8d, p. 18; *Handbook of the Collections*, Nelson Gallery and Atkins Museum, Kansas City, Mo., 1959, p. 241; *Khmer Sculpture* (New York), No. 5(к), pl. 22.

Nelson-Atkins Gallery of Art, Kansas City, Mo.; Nelson Fund.

19 FEMALE TORSO
    Early Baphuon style, first quarter of the eleventh century
    Dark gray sandstone; H. 15½ in.

This exquisite female torso represents Baphuon style at its best. The sculpture displays great sensitivity in the rendering of the female body which, combined with a very delicate carving, gives an astonishing effect. Because of the high polish of the stone, the skin has an effect of sensuous smoothness which contrasts effectively with the deliberately rough texture used to represent cloth.

The skirt, narrowly pleated, in a true Baphuon manner bares the belly and rises high at the back. This skirt, originally of full ankle-length (like Nos. 20, 27), folds in front to form a fish-tail panel. The skirt is supported by a jeweled belt fastened with a cord. Here it is of fairly simple type characteristic of the early Baphuon style (Bibl. 4, p. 133, pl. xxx, 2, and p. 75, pl. xvi, 1 and 2) as opposed to that of the late Baphuon style in which the belt is decorated with hanging jeweled pendants, as in Nos. 26, 27. The skirt shows traces of gilding, apparently a later application.

Cf. Bibl. 4, pl. 57A.

Publ. and Exh.: Sculpture of India (exhibition, Poughkeepsie, New York: Vassar College Art Gallery, April–May 1939), No. 22; Andrew C. Ritchie, *Catalogue of the Paintings and Sculpture, Albright Art Gallery*, Buffalo, 1949, pp. 126, 127; Henry Trubner, "The Art of Greater India," *Oriental Art*, vol. III, No. 1 (1950), pp. 33–39, fig. 4 on p. 37; *The Art of Greater India* (Los Angeles), No. 149.

Albright-Knox Art Gallery, Buffalo.

20 FEMALE FIGURE
    Early Baphuon style, first quarter of the eleventh century
    Grayish-green stone; H. 38¾ in.

This female figure relates quite closely to No. 19. The manner in which the skirt is arranged points also to an early Baphuon style (Bibl. 4, p. 75, pl. xvi, 1, and pl. 57-A). The unusual feature is that the skirt is not pleated, a rare phenomenon among the female figures of the Baphuon school.

Collection of Mr. and Mrs. John D. Rockefeller 3rd, New York.

21 ŚIVA
    Style of Baphuon, first half of the eleventh century
    Gray sandstone; H. 30¼ in.

Unlike the two preceding female figures which represent the early Baphuon style, Śiva provides an example of its maturity.

The slim body of the god is surmounted by a large head. The short *sampot*, with a highly stylized pocket fold on the left hip, is supported by a belt and rises high in the back; these are characteristics of the developed Baphuon style (Bibl. 4, p. 47, pl. VIII and p. 115, pl. XXIV, 2). Śiva's hair is piled high and tied into a knot formed from the braided locks. The face, with clearly drawn features, has a large mouth and big eyes, which are incised rather than carved. The god wears a close-cut beard ending in a point on the chin. The long ear lobes are now broken off. Lightly incised around the neck are three beauty lines, and a third eye is etched on the forehead.

Cf. Bibl. 6, p. 235.

Publ.: Handbook of The Cleveland Museum of Art (1958), No. 788; *Handbook of The Cleveland Museum of Art* (1966), p. 242.

The Cleveland Museum of Art; Purchase from the J. H. Wade Fund.

22 ŚIVA
    Style of Baphuon, first half of the eleventh century
    Stone; H. 53 in.

This classic Baphuon sculpture of Śiva is related in almost every detail to No. 21. It is perhaps somewhat more perfect and hence a fraction more explicit, as in the treatment of such details as the coiffure and the facial features.

Collection of Mr. and Mrs. Ben Heller, New York.

23 STANDING MALE FIGURE
    Style of Baphuon, first half of the eleventh century
    Buff sandstone; H. 28½ in.

Another Baphuon sculpture is of the same type as Nos. 20 and 22, lacking, however, the insignias of Śiva. There is no sign of the third eye on this figure's forehead, and the treatment of the hair is simplified. A high knot of hair, the Cambodian version of Śiva's *jaṭāmakuṭa*, is replaced here by a very flat arrangement. This may imply that the sculpture depicts a secular rather than a religious personage.

Publ. and Exh.: Masterpieces of Sculpture (exhibition, Minneapolis: Minneapolis Institute of Arts, November 1–December 11, 1949); *Art in Asia and the West* (San Francisco), No. 8F, illus. p. 18; *Handbook of the Collections*, Nelson Gallery and Atkins Museum, Kansas City, Mo., 1959, p. 238; *Khmer Sculpture* (New York), No. 6(к), p. 23.

Nelson-Atkins Gallery, Kansas City, Mo.; Nelson Fund.

24 HEAD OF BRAHMANICAL DEITY
    Style of Baphuon, first half of the eleventh century
    Sandstone; H. 9 5/16 in.

The head has plaited hair, coiled on the top into a round chignon which is held by a decorative ring. The front part of this chignon has been broken off, while the head was split through. This damage is now mended.

The sharply drawn face has the distinctive Baphuon features discussed in connection with No. 21. These are a large sensuous mouth, rather narrow and long eyes marked by incised double lines, softly arching eyebrows, and a straight nose, now partially damaged. The ears once had longer lobes. Although the coiffure suggests Śiva's "matted locks" it cannot be determined with certainty that he was the deity represented. There is even a possibility that it may be a female head.

Cf. Bibl. 4, pl. 59.

The George P. Bickford Collection, Cleveland.

25 HEAD OF BUDDHA
Style of Baphuon, first half of the eleventh century
Dark stone; H. 9⅝ in.

The general shape of this head and the treatment of various facial features are the same as in the Brahmanical head, No. 24. Even the details, such as the form of the hairline, are the same in both cases. The only obvious difference is in the hair itself, arranged here in the snail-like curls typical of a Buddha. The curls are organized methodically in alternating rows, the whorls of one row going towards the left and those of the other row towards the right. On the top of the head is the pointed *ushnīsha*.

The first half of the eleventh century was marked by a revival of Mahāyānism and a greater than ever syncretism of this religion with Śaivism. That this was the case seems to be proven by the patronage of Buddhism by King Suryavarman I, who reigned from 1002 to 1050 (Bibl. 9, p. 167). Buddhist sculptures are therefore quite common during this period.

Nelson-Atkins Gallery, Kansas City, Mo.; Nelson Fund.

26 MALE FIGURE
Late Baphuon style, third quarter of the eleventh century
Green sandstone; H. 52½ in.

A new feature appearing in this sculpture and not observed in previous Baphuon pieces is an ornamented belt decorated with a row of hanging pendants (Bibl. 4, p. 133, pl. XXX, 3). This type of belt appears for the first time in late Baphuon style and is seen very frequently in Angkor Vat sculpture. The treatment of the torso and the columnar legs is like that in earlier Baphuon figures.

Collection of Mr. and Mrs. John D. Rockefeller 3rd, New York.

27 FEMALE FIGURE
Late Baphuon style, third quarter of the eleventh century
Sandstone; H. 36 in.

This figure can be considered as a female counterpart to the male statue of the late Baphuon style (No. 26). She wears the same kind of elaborate belt with pendants which is characteristic of the late Baphuon school.

The waistline of the *sarong* is of rounded shape as opposed to the more oval form of the earlier Baphuon sculptures. The frontal panel formed by the gathered drapery is not straight as before but curves in a nervous way (Bibl. 4, p. 75, pl. XVI, 3). Finally the

breasts are smaller and less full, and there are no beauty lines, which in earlier examples usually appeared below the breast.

Cf. Bibl. 24, p. 209, cat. 27 and p. 210, cat. 29.

Collection of Mr. I. Kahane, Dobbs Ferry, N.Y.

28 PERHAPS BHAISAJYAGURU (BUDDHA OF HEALING)
Style of Angkor Vat, first half of the twelfth century
Bronze; H. 23 in.

During the Angkorean Period one of the most common representations of Buddha shows him in the pose of meditation (*dhyānāsana*), seated on the coils of the multi-headed serpent, Mucalinda. The Buddha is adorned with all the princely ornaments, such as the crown, a handsome girdle with pendants, earrings, necklace, armlets, wristlets, and anklets.

In this case he wears also an upper garment of *sanghati* (monk's robe) type which is drawn over the left shoulder, with a rectangular lappet hanging from it. The iconography of the figure presents a problem. It is possible that this stele may represent the Buddha of Healing, Bhaisajyaguru, who is the only Buddha mentioned in the epigraphy of Jayavarman VII and who was apparently quite popular during the reign of this ruler (Bibl. 7, p. 301). The flask with a slightly pointed top in the upturned palm of the Buddha's right hand, which is a symbol of Bhaisajyaguru, may speak in favor of this theory. On the other hand, this jar appears in the hands of Buddhas on many occasions and is not sufficient to make a definite iconographical attribution (Marcus, "Buddha Sheltered by Mucalinda," p. 185). The presence of the naga in these figures may symbolize the protective power associated with serpents (*Ibid.*, pp. 186, 187). The figure is a portable image in the round (*chala chitra*) and can be viewed from all sides. It is cast in three parts—the figure, the hollow coils, and the solid hood. There are still traces of gilding on the incisions of the naga's scales.

Publ.: 6 Soi Kasemsan II, An Illustrated Survey of the Bangkok Home of James H. W. Thompson, rev. 2nd ed., January 1962, pp. 30, 31; *Bulletin of The Cleveland Museum of Art*, vol. L (December 1963), illus. p. 287; "Oriental Art Recently Acquired by American Museums, 1963," *Archives of the Chinese Art Society of America*, vol. XVIII (1964), p. 73, fig. 16; Marcus, "Buddha Sheltered by Mucalinda," pp. 185–193; *Idem.* "Buddha Sheltered by Mucalinda," *The Burlington Magazine*, vol. CVIII (May 1966), pp. 258, 261, illus. p. 263; *Handbook of The Cleveland Museum of Art* (1966), p. 243; *Selected Works: The Cleveland Museum of Art* (1967), pl. 47.

The Cleveland Museum of Art; John L. Severance Fund.

29 BUDDHA SHELTERED BY MUCALINDA
Style of Angkor Vat, first half of the twelfth century
Bronze; H. 16½ in.

This stele is very similar to the Cleveland Buddha (No. 28). It differs in a few details; for instance, Buddha does not carry a jar in his hands, his torso is bare, and his *sampot* is longer, reaching below the knees. The position in which he sits, his ornaments, and the seven-headed naga hood are exactly the same as in the previous figure (No. 28). The youthful, slightly smiling face depicts the same physical features as the Cleveland sculpture—straight nose, large, fleshy mouth, double-outlined eyes, and natural eyebrow arches. The body, well rounded and powerful, is equally as harmonious as that of No. 28. The slightly hieratic feeling of the figure is characteristic of the period in general and typical of this kind of image. Steles like this were often votive offerings given with the hope of acquiring personal merit. Their function was that of an altar, which would explain their somewhat static and often hieratic character.

Collection of Mr. and Mrs. John D. Rockefeller 3rd, New York.

30 BUDDHA ENTHRONED
Style of Angkor Vat, first half of the twelfth century
Bronze; H. 10½ in.

This altarpiece belongs to a group of bronzes which were excavated together at a site near Saigon. They were buried there most probably sometime during the Siamese invasions in the fifteenth century. Other objects from the same hoard in this exhibition are the Garuda and Vishnu from Detroit (Nos. 33, 39), the Jambhala from Philadelphia (No. 36), and the Lakshmi from Kansas City (No. 38). (The remaining sculptures are the altarpiece with Buddha from the Freer Gallery of Art, Washington; the ritual bell from the Boston Museum of Fine Arts, see Sherman E. Lee, "A Cambodian Bronze Hoard," *Art in America*, vol. XXXI, No. 2 [April 1943], pp. 78–83, figs. 1, 2; and the dancing apsara, present location unknown [Fig. 15]). This, however, does not mean that all of them belong stylistically to the same period.

Buddha sits on a throne which has as a background a shallow niche. This niche consists of two pilasters supporting a *makara torana* which is outlined by flames (*jvalas*). In the niche directly above Buddha's head is a small wheel in relief which, no doubt, refers to the First Sermon of Buddha at the Deer Park in Banares, and so to Buddha's act in first "Turning the Wheel of the Law." At the top of the altar is a Bodhi tree, symbolizing Buddha's Enlightenment. Both the figure of Buddha and the Bodhi tree are detachable. Buddha is seated in the *dhyānāsana mudrā* (pose of meditation). As is frequently the case in Cambodian sculpture he is nude to the waist, and he wears the usual ornaments. On the palm of his right hand is an indeterminate object which could be either a lotus bud or a medicine jar, like that carried by Bhaisajyaguru (No. 28).

It is possible that the altar in its present form is not quite complete, and that it once rested on a stand similar to that of the Freer Gallery bronze mentioned above, possibly, like the latter, decorated with figures of the twenty-four mortal Buddhas.

Cf. No. 61.

Publ. and Exh.: Buddhist Art (exhibition, Detroit: Detroit Institute of Arts, October 1942), pp. 26, 50, No. 31, illus.; Lee, "A Cambodian Bronze Hoard," p. 80, fig. 3; Hollis, "A Cambodian Bronze Altarpiece," *Bulletin of The Cleveland Museum of Art*, vol. XXXI (September 1944), pp. 138, 139; *The Art of Greater India* (Los Angeles), No. 152; *Bronzes of India and Greater India* (exhibition, Providence, R.I.: Rhode Island School of Design, 1955), No. 46; *Handbook of The Cleveland Museum of Art* (1958), No. 790; *Khmer Sculpture* (New York), No. 24K, illus. p. 49; *Handbook of The Cleveland Museum of Art* (1966), p. 242.

The Cleveland Museum of Art; Purchase from the J. H. Wade Fund.

31 VAJRASATTVA
Style of Angkor Vat, first half of the twelfth century
Bronze; H. 5 in.

Vajrasattva, or Buddha of Supreme Intelligence, is often included in a group of Dhyāni Buddhas and considered to be a spiritual son of Akshobya. Judging from bronze statuettes of Vajrasattva found fairly frequently in the vicinity of Angkor, his cult must have been quite popular during this period.

He is seated with his legs locked, holding in the right hand against his breast a *vajra* (thunderbolt). His left hand holds a *ghaṇṭa* (bell) on his hip. Vajrasattva wears all the princely ornaments of Bodhisattva, as does Bhaisajyaguru, or the Buddha sheltered by the naga. These ornaments and details of costume are very deeply incised and project boldly from the surface of the bronze. The figure was probably originally seated on a lotus pedestal which is now missing. The patina, a brilliant blue green, while fortuitous, cannot be overlooked in evaluating the quality of the image.

Cf. Bibl. 24, p. 141, fig. 83.

Collection of Mr. and Mrs. John D. Rockefeller 3rd, New York.

32 FOUR-ARMED FEMALE DIVINITY
Style of Angkor Vat, first half of the twelfth century
Bronze; H. 8 3/16 in.

The deity's four hands lack attributes, which makes an iconographical identification impossible. In various details of costume the sculpture recalls reliefs of the celestial apsaras from the walls of Angkor Vat (Fig. 20), but those figures as a rule have only two hands.

The divinity wears a tall tiara and a loin cloth which is pulled out above the girdle to create a butterfly-like flare at the right hip (Bibl. 4, p. 79, pl. XVII, 3). Earrings, a three-stranded necklace with a medallion in the front and a pendant in the back, armbands, bracelets, anklets, and a decorative girdle complete her attire.

The George P. Bickford Collection, Cleveland.

33 GARUDA
Style of Angkor Vat, first half of the twelfth century
Bronze; H. 9¾ in.

The sacred bird and vehicle of Vishnu, Garuda, is represented as a winged god, half man and half beast. He is depicted in his *vāhana* role, striding forward, with his arms raised above his shoulders.

This type of representation of Garuda in bronze became fairly common from the end of the eleventh century onward and persisted during the Angkorean Period (Bibl. 7, p. 309). In Bayon, however, Garuda is more frequently depicted in association with a naga on finials (Nos. 57, 59). Garuda was often used in Cambodian art as a decorative motif. Various ritual objects, for instance the handles of bells, were decorated with Garuda figures (Bibl. 10, pl. XLI). This is where many smaller bronzes of Garuda originate. Garuda was also depicted very often in stone sculpture, particularly from Banteay Srei onwards. (Heinrich Zimmer, *The Art of Indian Asia*, New York, 1955, p. 523). One may say that in later Cambodian art he became a symbol of Khmer imperial power.

Publ. and Exh.: Sculpture of India (Vassar), No. 24; Lee, "A Cambodian Bronze Garuda," *Bulletin of the Detroit Institute of Arts*, vol. XXIII, No. 1 (October 1943), pp. 12–14; Lee, *Art of India, China, and Japan*, The Detroit Institute of Arts, Detroit 1946, p. 14, fig. 11; Trubner, "The Art of Greater India," fig. 6 on p. 37; *The Art of Greater India* (Los Angeles), No. 151; *Art in Asia and the West* (San Francisco), No. 8d, illus. p. 18.

The Detroit Institute of Arts; Gift of Albert Kahn.

34   METAL FINIAL
   Style of Angkor Vat, first half of the twelfth century
   Bronze; H. 20⅞ in.

Cambodian architecture and most of the sculpture which has survived to our day were done in stone; occasionally images were cast in bronze or other metals. This, however, does not mean that other materials such as wood were not used. As a matter of fact, while stone was used mostly for religious buildings—temples, etc.—wood was usually employed for secular architecture, furniture, and various objects of daily use. It is not surprising that wood, an easily perishable material, rarely survived. It was, however, in this wooden architecture and in the production of furniture that metal was richly employed as a decorative factor. Often parts of terraces, balustrades, eaves of roofs, bows of boats, or furniture finials were made of bronze. The most favored motifs used in these terminals were nagas, garudas, or other types of beasts. This one, with small head and gracefully curved neck, which almost resembles the neck of a swan, may be a terminal of a boat not at all unlike those depicted in Angkor reliefs (Fig. 12).

Seattle Art Museum; Eugene Fuller Memorial Collection.

35.   VISHNU ON GARUDA
   Transition from Angkor Vat to Angkor Thom Period, second half of the twelfth century
   Gilt bronze; H. 6⅝ in.

Vishnu, with four arms, stands on the shoulders of the winged Garuda who walks forward. Vishnu holds his usual attributes—a *chakra* (wheel) in his uplifted right hand, a *śanka* (conch) in the upper left hand, and a *gadā* (mace) in the lower left hand. The lower right hand expresses *varada mudrā*, the gift-bestowing gesture. Garuda's arms are raised and his tail feathers curve up and are held to his back with a looped rod. The wing feathers are clearly modeled whereas those on his haunches are incised. The bronze clearly shows traces of gilding which, as mentioned earlier (No. 8), was one of the common decorative techniques in Cambodian bronzes.

   Cf. Bibl. 10, pls. XLII, XLIII, 2 and 3.

The George P. Bickford Collection, Cleveland.

36   JAMBHALA
   Transition from Angkor Vat to Angkor Thom Period, second half of the twelfth century
   Bronze; H. 8⅛ in.

Jambhala, a Buddhist equivalent of the Hindu god of wealth, Kuvera, is represented as a corpulent and bejeweled deity. The god stands in frontal position on a lotus pedestal of unusual shape,

with both hands raised in *abhaya mudrā*, the gesture of protection. He wears a pointed crown on his head, a cloak over his shoulders, and a long skirt supported by a jeweled belt.

Stylistically, the sculpture belongs to the transition between the two Angkorean periods. The type of crown and ornaments are still in the Angkor Vat tradition whereas the face, with heavily marked eyebrows, large mouth, and smiling expression, reflects the new tendencies brought in by the Bayon sculpture.

   Publ. and Exh.: Buddhist Art (Detroit), p. 26, No. 32; Lee, "A Cambodian Bronze Hoard," fig. 4; *The Art of Greater India* (Los Angeles), No. 153.

Philadelphia Museum of Art.

37   CONCH
   Transition from Angkor Vat to Angkor Thom Period, second half of the twelfth century
   Bronze; H. 10½ in.

The conches of this type served Cambodians as cult objects. The conch was used both as a musical instrument and as a receptacle to hold holy water during the various rituals.

The shapes of these conches are relatively uniform; the base is spiral, and the mouth holds a panel decorated in relief—in this case with a male dancer performing on a lotus flower. The details of his costume indicate a date in the second half of the twelfth century.

   Cf. Bibl. 7, pl. LVIII, 2; Bibl. 10, pl. XXXVI.

Museum of Fine Arts, Boston; Helen S. Coolidge Fund.

38   LAKSHMI (?)
   Early Bayon style, late twelfth century
   Bronze; H. 9¼ in.

Because of the coexistence of Hinduism and Buddhism in Cambodia and the syncretism of these two religions, it is sometimes impossible to distinguish between their deities unless they carry their respective attributes. The goddess here is either Lakshmi, the consort of Vishnu, or Prājñāpāramitā, the Buddhist goddess of Transcendent Wisdom. Both divinities wear the same type of *jaṭa* and ornaments, and may be depicted with the third eye on the forehead (Bibl. 33, pl. XVI, 2). Both may carry a lotus bud in the left hand. Were the other hand of this deity intact, the identification would be simple since Lakshmi would carry a lotus bud in each hand and Prājñāpāramitā would be distinguished by either the *vitarka mudrā*, a book, or a flask. As it is, there is no certain way of identifying the goddess. The probability of the figure being Lakshmi is, however, suggested by the fact that it seems to match perfectly, both in height and style, the figure of Vishnu (No. 39). If we remember that these bronzes were excavated together (see No. 30), it seems to be highly probable that this figure is a mate to Vishnu and therefore his *śakti*, Lakshmi.

   Publ. and Exh.: Buddhist Art (Detroit) cat. 34; Lee, "A Cambodian Bronze Hoard," fig. 6.

Nelson-Atkins Gallery, Kansas City, Mo.; Nelson Fund.

39 STANDING VISHNU
Early Bayon style, late twelfth century
Bronze; H. 9 1/16 in.

Vishnu, the Preserver, is represented with four arms carrying his usual attributes, discus (*chakra*) and conch (*śanka*) in his upper hands, and lotus bud (*padma*) and mace (*gadā*) in his lower hands. The third eye in the forehead and the high coiffure are other signs typical of Brahmanical deities.

In some details, the style of the bronze still relates to the Angkor Vat bronzes, but in others it reflects pure Bayon characteristics. The facial type particularly is not too far removed from the Angkor Vat style. The *sampot* (Bibl. 4, p. 59, pl. XIII, 2), however, and the convention of marking the knee by an incision of a semicircle are unmistakable Bayon features. Considering these cross influences of the first and second Angkorean phase, it seems appropriate to ascribe the bronze to the end of the twelfth century.

Cf. No. 38 and Bibl. 24, p. 142, fig. 84.

Publ.: Lee, "A Cambodian Bronze Hoard," fig. 5.

The Detroit Institute of Arts.

40 PART OF A LINTEL WITH RĀMĀYANA SCENE
Style of Angkor Thom, late twelfth century
Red sandstone; H. 35 in. W. 74 in.

The scene depicted in relief is probably from the Rāmāyana and shows Rāvana, the demon of Lanka, being attacked by the army of monkeys. Originally, Rāvana filled the center of the complete composition, which is kept fairly symmetrical. The relief is quite deep but more or less on one level without variation and graduation of planes. It is intentionally decorative which seems to be the main concern of the artist. There is an attempt at depicting action and movement, but these are secondary values. It is the decorative pattern that matters, the usual *horror vacui* that caused the entire surface of the stone to be covered with a thick network of relief. The technique of the stone carving at Angkor Thom in general is somewhat inferior in comparison to the earlier reliefs of Angkor Vat. The proliferation of picturesque detail is responsible for the clumsier execution. In this case, however, the action is particularly animated and convincing. This may be because it is still fairly close to the Angkor Vat tradition. The type of *sampot* worn by Rāvana is of the second Angkorean Period, but the decorative ornaments on the chest appear in both Angkor Vat and Angkor Thom sculpture. The head of Rāvana, both face and crown, is a replacement and therefore provides no stylistic clue.

Center of Asian Art and Culture, City and County of San Francisco; Avery Brundage Collection.

41 FRIEZE WITH APSARAS
Style of Bayon, late twelfth–early thirteenth century
Sandstone; H. 10 in., W. 34½ in.

It is true of Cambodian sculpture in general and Angkorean work in particular that it consists primarily of reliefs which are a part of architecture, and therefore are scarce in western collections. Fortunately, they remain in the places of their origin and are less frequently represented here. This lacuna could form the erroneous impression that sculpture in the round flourished more than did relief carving in Cambodia.

This frieze, depicting four dancers entwined with garlands and a *makara* on the right side, provides, as does No. 40, an example of decorative sculpture in the service of architecture. Such relief sculpture can be categorized into various groups. The narrative scenes, and the purely decorative ones which have the sole purpose of filling the architectural space, are the two most important categories. This lintel belongs to the latter group. The apsaras are placed in a row in similar dancing positions. Their hands are raised in a "supporting" gesture and they seem to act as atlantes which is quite appropriate for figures decorating an architectural frieze. Even though a certain amount of repetition is necessary for this type of decorative frieze, variations in the gestures and a feeling for movement overcome monotony. All that can be hoped for in architectural sculpture is achieved here.

The figures are typically Bayon in character with their high tiaras, the particular kind of *sampot*, and the physiognomy with the mysterious Bayon smile. A good stylistic comparison to this piece is the well known frieze of the same theme from the Musée Guimet in Paris (M. M. Deneck, *Indian Sculpture*, London, 1962, pls. 223, 224).

Publ. and Exh.: Hollis, "A Frieze from Angkor," *Bulletin of The Cleveland Museum of Art*, vol. XXVII (January 1940), pp. 4, 5, illus. p. 2; R. Shoolman and C. E. Slatkin, *Enjoyment of Art in America*, Philadelphia/New York, 1942, pl. 122; *Dance Index*, vol. VI, No. 4 (April 1947), p. 78; *Handbook of The Cleveland Museum of Art* (1958), No. 791; *Khmer Sculpture* (New York), No. 18(K), illus. pp. 28, 29; *Art News* (December 1961), illus. p. 44; *Handbook of The Cleveland Museum of Art* (1966), p. 242.

The Cleveland Museum of Art; Purchase from the J. H. Wade Fund.

42 FRAGMENT OF A PILLAR WITH DANCING APSARAS
Style of Bayon, late twelfth–early thirteenth century
Limestone; H. 33 in., W. 16½ in.

The two apsaras are carved in very low relief. The placement of the figures in a highly decorative niche, their mirror-image poses, and their costumes are characteristics of the Bayon style. Pillars of this type are quite commonplace in Bayon and much comparative material can be found (Figs. 6, 7 and Bibl. 24, p. 241). A counterpart in bronze sculpture is the figure of a dancing apsara from the Ross Collection in the Museum of Fine Arts, Boston, which dates to the same period (Bibl. 14, pl. XXII).

Publ.: *Bulletin of the Metropolitan Museum of Art*, vol. XXXII, No. 4 (April 1937), p. 86, fig. 3.

The Metropolitan Museum of Art, New York; Fletcher Fund, 1935.

43 RELIEF OF APSARA
Probably from the terrace of the Leper King, late twelfth–early thirteenth century
Sandstone: H. 24 in., W. 13 in.

This relief sculpture, now incomplete, depicts a bust of a celestial apsara or of a princess. She wears a tall tiara and is richly adorned with beaded ear ornaments and earrings, necklaces, and armbands. There is a suggestion of a smile on her face. The figure recalls in every detail the female portraits from the walls of the terrace of the Leper King (Fig. 16).

Publ.: Hollis, "A Cambodian Royal Sculpture," *Bulletin of The Cleveland Museum of Art*, vol. xxv (November 1938), pp. 163, 164; *Parnassus* (January 1939), p. 39, left; *Handbook of The Cleveland Museum of Art* (1958), No. 792; *Handbook of The Cleveland Museum of Art* (1966), p. 243.

The Cleveland Museum of Art; Purchase from the J. H. Wade Fund.

44 FIGURE OF A HERMIT
Style of Bayon, late twelfth–early thirteenth century
Stone; H. 20 in.

The total lack of ornaments and the reduction of clothing to a strip around the hips suggest that the figure represents an ascetic. This seems to be further confirmed by the sign of "Om" on the *jaṭāmakuṭa*, as well as by the unshaven face. The face with its smiling, mystical expression is characteristic of the Bayon style. The body is fairly rigid and inexpressive, partially due to the fact that the limbs are missing. It seems, however, that the artist purposely concentrated on the bare essentials when sculpting the figure, stressing the physiognomy more and achieving by these means a feeling of austerity appropriate to a figure of a Śaivite ascetic.

Cf. Fig. 17.

Anonymous Loan.

45 GUARDIAN LION
Style of Bayon, late twelfth–early thirteenth century
Sandstone; H. 29½ in.

The lion became popular as a temple guardian in Cambodian art from the Kulen style onwards (Bibl. 7, p. 311). Since it has never been native to Cambodia it took on the character of a somewhat fantastic beast in Khmer art.

The lion represented here is of Bayon type. Its mouth is wide open, with lips drawn back giving the impression of a grin. Its head remains more a *kirttimukha* (mask of glory) than a true lion's head. The massive chest is covered by a decorative mane. The beast is seated in a rigid attitude quite appropriate to its function as a temple guardian (see Fig. 18).

Collection of R. Hatfield Ellsworth and James R. Goldie, New York.

46 HEAD OF BUDDHA
Angkor Thom, late twelfth–early thirteenth century
Sandstone; H. 13½ in.

Cambodian art during its entire evolution was marked by a parallel development of both Hindu and Buddhist sculpture. While Hinduism for many centuries dominated as the state religion, Buddhist art continued its existence with varying fortunes. In the reign of Jayavarman VII, however, Mahāyāna Buddhism became dominant. During the rule of this king, the Bayon temple was erected at his capital of Angkor Thom, and the most common representations of this period are figures of Buddha, Lokeśvara, Prājñāparamitā, Vajrasattva, and the whole Mahāyānic assemblage.

This head of Buddha reflects one of the set patterns for the representations of Buddha characteristic of this period. The face is round with regular features, eyes outlined by a double, incised line, and large mouth with the corners raised in a smile. The hair, in conventional curls, rises to a pointed *ushnīsha*, and forms points at the temples. The eyes here are open; the tendency in many sculptures is to depict them closed which creates the feeling of meditative concentration (Nos. 47–50). The mysterious Bayon smile lightens the face, giving it a benevolent expression.

Publ.: William E. Ward, "Head of Buddha," *Bulletin of The Cleveland Museum of Art*, vol. xxxix (October 1952), pp. 205–207, illus. p. 203.

The Cleveland Museum of Art; Purchase from the J. H. Wade Fund.

47 HEAD OF BUDDHA
Style of Bayon, late twelfth–early thirteenth century
Stone; H. 8½ in.

Basically, this head of Buddha repeats the same type as No. 46, but is perhaps more individualized and advances more toward naturalism. In fact, it is more a human head with almost personalized facial features and strong native Cambodian flavor. It is also more "sculptural" and less schematized than No. 46. The hair depicted in the convention of little, multiple knobs gives more plasticity than does the incised pattern of curly hair; the hairline is natural and not geometricized as in No. 46.

Publ. and Exh.: Fogg Art Museum, Handbook, Cambridge, Mass., 1931 ed., p. 142, 1936 ed., p. 174; Bibl. 14, p. 237, No. 21 and pl. xix-b; Denman W. Ross, "An Example of Cambodian Sculpture," *Fogg Art Museum Notes* (June 1922), pp. 3–13, illus. pls. 1 and 2; *The Evolution of the Buddha Image* (exhibition, New York: Asia House Gallery, May 6–June 30, 1963), No. 29.

Fogg Art Museum, Harvard University, Cambridge, Mass.; Gift of Paul J. Sachs.

48 FRAGMENT OF A HEAD
Style of Bayon, late twelfth–early thirteenth century
Stone; H. 9½ in.

This fragment of a male head—probably that of a Buddha—although very incomplete, gives another version of the Bayon sculptural type. The stylized, bead-shaped locks arranged in vertical rows, the thick projecting eyebrows, the closed eyes with well-formed lids, and the sensuous mouth with its corners raised in a smile, point to the same artistic trend as is reflected in No. 52. In connection with this comparison it may be interesting to observe a difference in the hairline in No. 52, which is of rounder shape and which is, according to Groslier, characteristic of female heads (Bibl. 14, p. 240, footnote).

Cf. Bibl. 41, figs. 189 and 190.

Collection of Mr. Robert Rousset, Paris.

49 BUST OF BUDDHA WITH NAGA HOOD
   Style of Bayon, reportedly from Chausay Temple, late
      twelfth–early thirteenth century
   Limestone; H. 35 in.

The sculpture is reported to be from the Chausay Tevada temple which dates to the time of Angkor Vat. The Buddha shows, however, characteristics of the fully matured Bayon style. If from the Chausay temple, it belongs to its Bayon phase. The iconography is the same as that of the Angkor Vat bronzes discussed earlier (Nos. 28, 29). The sculpture is incomplete today, but there is no doubt that it was originally a full figure seated on the snake coil. The face with closed eyes, wide mouth, and meditative smile, and the convention of incised curls crowned by a pointed *ushnīsha*, are indicative of the Bayon style. The Buddha is adorned with heavy earrings but he does not wear a necklace as he did in the Angkor Vat images. This lack of ornaments, frequent during this period, is another characteristic of Bayon sculpture.

Publ.: Alan Priest, "A Collection of Cambodian Sculpture," *Bulletin of The Metropolitan Museum of Art*, vol. XXXII, No. 4 (April 1937), pp. 84–88, illus. cover.

The Metropolitan Museum of Art, New York; Fletcher Fund, 1935.

50 HEAD OF LOKEŚVARA
   Style of Bayon, late twelfth–early thirteenth century
   Pink sandstone: H. 13⅞ in.

We mentioned earlier that Lokeśvara was the object of a flourishing cult in Cambodia during the Angkorean Period. The frequency with which his image appears, especially at Angkor Thom, Banteay Chmar, and Nak Pan, points to him as one of the most important gods if not the main deity of the Bayon Period.

The hair of Lokeśvara is drawn into a high chignon with a pattern of incised waves, typical for the period. The *makuṭa* is decorated with the figure of a Dhyāni Buddha, Amitābha, now partially damaged like the rest of the high chignon. The eyes of the beautifully executed face are almost closed, but as is often the case with Bayon sculptures which have closed or semi-closed eyes, the upper lid is carefully rounded in a manner which makes one feel the presence of the eyeball underneath. The natural arches of the eyebrows, straight nose, large mouth, and a contemplative smile have been noted before as characteristics of the Bayon school.

Cf. Bibl. 41, figs. 191, 201.

Publ.: Ward, "Buddhist Head," *Bulletin of The Cleveland Museum of Art*, vol. XLIII (January 1956), pp. 5, 6, illus. p. 2; *Handbook of The Cleveland Museum of Art* (1958), No. 789; Marcus, "Buddha Sheltered by Mucalinda," (*Bulletin, Cleveland Museum of Art*) p. 192, fig. 11; *Handbook of The Cleveland Museum of Art* (1966), p. 243.

The Cleveland Museum of Art; Purchase from the J. H. Wade Fund.

51 BUST OF THE ELEVEN-HEADED AVALOKITEŚVARA
   Style of Angkor Thom, from Porte des Mortes, late twelfth–
      early thirteenth century
   Grayish limestone; H. 52 in.

The sculpture, incomplete as it is today, was probably meant to represent the eleven-headed Avalokiteśvara, one of the very popular forms of this Bodhisattva whose cult flourished during the second Angkorean period. It now has seven heads, the top, obviously, having been broken off. There is one empty space with no face on the back of the figure, apparently premeditated since the sculpture otherwise is finished, and so we may infer that the figure originally was crowned with another four-faced piece, making a total of eleven heads. (Priest, "A Collection of Cambodian Sculpture," p. 85, suggests that the sculpture represents Hevajra.)

This beautifully serene sculpture illustrates one of the high achievements reached by Cambodian artists during the second Angkorean phase. Avalokiteśvara's faces recall to one's mind the colossal smiling faces from the towers of Bayon which overlook the four cardinal points (fig. 8). The faces have a somewhat native Cambodian flavor; they are broad with high cheeks, have flat noses with broad nostrils, and large lips. The eyes, outlined by the incised, double line but with well-rendered pupils, are somewhat narrow and give an impression of looking downward. The Bodhisattva's name, Avalokiteśvara, variously translated means "the lord who looks down" and "the lord with compassionate glances" which in itself gives a perfect description of this deity.

Publ.: Priest, "A Collection of Cambodian Sculpture," fig. 4.

The Metropolitan Museum of Art, New York; Fletcher Fund, 1935.

52 HEAD OF PRĀJÑĀPARAMITĀ
   Style of Bayon, late twelfth–early thirteenth century
   Sandstone; H. 14 9/16 in.

Prājñāparamitā, the Goddess of Transcendent Wisdom, is a deity which, along with Avalokiteśvara (her male counterpart), was hugely popular during the second Angkorean period. Here she is depicted with the usual mystical Bayon smile and closed eyes, a sign of meditative concentration.

The divinity's headdress is conventionalized in Bayon manner, with braids stylized into crescents. At the top of the head is the *ushnīsha* against which is placed a seated image of Akshobya. The facial features are another unmistakable characteristic of the Bayon style, particularly the thick and sharply drawn eyebrows and the large mouth with its corners slightly raised in a smile. The figure shows a strong affiliation with the famous Bayon Prājñāparamitā in the Musée Guimet (Bibl. 41, fig. 189).

Publ.: *Bulletin de la Commission Archeologique de l'Indochine* (Paris, 1913), pl. I, 1; Bibl. 14, p. 240, No. 40, not illus.; *Bulletin of the Art Institute of Chicago*, vol. XVIII, No. 4 (April 1924), cover.

Art Institute of Chicago; S. M. Nickerson Collection.

53 (a) and (b) ROYAL COUPLE
Bayon style, late twelfth–early thirteenth century
Sandstone; (male) H. 54 in., (female) H. 55 in.

The figures seem to form a pair. They provide no clues as to their iconography but, judging from the presence of only two arms (now partially broken off) and a lack of any divine insignia, it may be assumed that they represent ordinary mortals. If so, they must be a royal pair since only personages of prominent social position would be portrayed in monumental sculpture of this type.

The sculptures reflect the usual characteristics of the Bayon school. The *sampot* of the male figure is of the same kind as is most commonly found among the Banteay Chmar male figures. The *makutas* of both figures are of the regular Bayon type and the same convention of depicting the braids is used (*cf.* No. 48). Also characteristically Bayon is the lack of ornament on the bodies and the facial types. In connection with the latter, it is interesting to remark that the smiling expression of these figures is different from that of the deities. While in religious figures it was a smile of gentle detachment and compassion, here it is a sardonic smile. The *asuras* and creatures of lower category displayed still another kind of smile—a grin—sometimes grotesque in its character (Fig. 13). It may be that the Bayon artists, great masters of physiognomy, made a purposeful distinction in these expressions, choosing them in accordance with the depicted subject matter.

Collection of Mr. and Mrs. John D. Rockefeller 3rd, New York.

54 BUDDHA SHELTERED BY MUCALINDA,
    BHAISAJYAGURU (?)
Style of Bayon, late twelfth–early thirteenth century
Bronze; H. 11½ in.

The stele with Buddha sheltered by Mucalinda is a Bayon version of exactly the same altar type known to us from the Angkor Vat period (Nos. 28, 29). The most noticeable difference is in the figure of Buddha himself. He sits in the same *dhyānāsana* position holding a medicine jar (?) in his right uplifted palm, but he is devoid of princely ornaments and wears monastic robes of a *sanghati* type drawn over his left shoulder. He does not wear the crown; instead his hair is braided into a pointed *ushnīsha*.

Publ.: Khmer Sculpture (New York,) No. 22(K), p. 46.

Collection of Dr. and Mrs. Samuel Eilenberg, New York.

55 VAJRASATTVA
Style of Angkor Thom, twelfth–thirteenth century
Bronze; H. 7¼ in.

Vajrasattva is seated in *dhyānāsana* on a double-petaled lotus base (*mahambuja pitha*) which is set on a rectangular pedestal. The right hand at his chest holds the *vajra* while the left one at his hip holds a *ghanta*, or bell. The deity wears a tiered crown, earrings, a necklace, armbands, bracelets, anklets, a high waistband, and a *sampot* which reaches to above the knee. From the back of the crown hang cords which coil on the shoulders, and from the back of the *sampot* belt cords of the same type hang and coil symmetrically over the legs on either side. A partly braided cord falls over the left shoulders and is looped into the high waistband. Behind the figure, on the lotus throne, there is a slot to hold the missing nimbus. In the details of costume and ornaments this bronze does not fit a standard pattern of the Bayon style. There-

fore, it is not surprising that its Cambodian origin had been questioned (Hollis, "A Javanese Bronze"; Bibl. 10, p. 44, pl. XXVII, 2). A closer examination, however, points to the definite characteristics of the second Angkorean period, especially the facial features of the figure reflecting the well-known smile which could not belong anywhere but with the Bayon sculptures.

Publ. and Exh.: Bibl. 10, p. 43, and pl. XXVII, 2; Hollis, "A Javanese Bronze," *Bulletin of The Cleveland Museum of Art*, vol. XXXV (October 1948), pp. 187, 188, illus. p. 185; *The Art of Greater India* (Los Angeles), No. 170; *Bronzes of India and Greater India* (Providence), No. 21, not illus.; *Khmer Sculpture* (New York), No. 19(K), p. 63, not illus.

The Cleveland Museum of Art; Purchase from the J. H. Wade Fund.

56 FINIAL WITH THE TEMPTATION OF BUDDHA BY
    MĀRA
Style of Bayon, late twelfth–early thirteenth century
Bronze; H. 15 7/16 in.

This bronze finial—its hollow base designed to be set on a pole or staff—has, in the center of the terminal, a Buddha seated on a lotus flower surrounded by a flaming mandorla. The stylized foliage above his head is meant to symbolize the Bodhi tree. The iconography refers to the temptation of Buddha by Māra, depicted here as a dancing figure below Buddha and accompanied by two demons. The temptation took place before Buddha's Enlightenment, while he was meditating under the Bodhi tree. It was then that Buddha called the Earth to witness, which is expressed by the gesture of his right hand, the *bhumisparsa mudrā*.

Publ.: Bulletin of The Cleveland Museum of Art, vol. LI (December 1964), No. 45, illus. p. 253, listed p. 262; Bibl. 7, pl. LIX, 2 (erroneously listed as belonging to the Bangkok Museum); *Handbook of The Cleveland Museum of Art* (1966), p. 242.

The Cleveland Museum of Art; Purchase, Andrew R. and Martha Holden Jennings Fund.

57 GARUDA TERMINAL
Style of Bayon, late twelfth–early thirteenth century
Bronze; H. 7⅛ in.

It was mentioned earlier (No. 34) that the usual Cambodian practice was to decorate wooden architecture and furniture with bronze ornaments. The feet and finials of furniture, the terminals of balustrades, etc., ended in naga or garuda heads, following the style of stone architecture (Fig. 19). An example of such a terminal is provided here by this Garuda finial of typical Bayon style.

Cf. Bibl. 7, pl. LIX, 1; Bibl. 41, fig. 67; Bibl. 8, fig. 3.

Collection of Mr. Peter Marks, New York.

58 PALANQUIN HOOK AND RING
Style of Bayon, late twelfth–early thirteenth century
Bronze; (hook) H. 8⅝ in., W. 3¼ in.; (ring) H. 6⅝ in.
    Diam. 7 in.

Hooks and suspension rings of this type were used as parts of harness, chariot ornaments, and palanquins. The bas reliefs of Angkor Vat, Bayon, Banteay Chmar and other temples depict diverse vehicles which were popular at this time. It is not difficult to reconstruct the usage of these parts on the basis of these reliefs.

This particular hook and ring probably come from a palanquin. Hooks like this were fixed by bolts to the ends of transverse poles carried on the shoulders of the bearers. The hooks supported suspension rings to which the litter was fastened.

The decoration of these bronze pieces is often very rich, particularly during the Bayon period. The decorative motifs applied are similar to those on other bronzes—nagas, garudas, feathers treated like foliage, etc. They were often gilded.

Cf. Bibl. 7, pl. LX; Bibl. 24, p. 161, pls. 92, 93.

Seattle Art Museum; Margaret E. Fuller Purchase Fund.

59 GARUDA FINIAL
    Style of Bayon, late twelfth–early thirteenth century
    Bronze; H. 9¼ in.

This Garuda finial belongs to the same category as the above bronzes (Nos. 34, 57, 58). Judging from its size, it probably served as a part of furniture or chariot decoration. In style it is very close to the palanquin set, also from the Seattle Museum.

Seattle Art Museum; Margaret E. Fuller Purchase Fund.

60 PILLAR WITH APSARA
    Post-Bayon style, thirteenth century
    Reddish sandstone; H. 30¾ in., W. 13 in.

Thirteenth-century Cambodian art is marked by eclecticism resulting in a gradual decadence of sculpture. After the death of Jayavarman VII, who was responsible for the development of the Bayon, this style persisted for some time but without its previous intensity and vigor. As is often the case with art which is in decline, it started to look backwards to the traditional styles for inspiration, archaizing "in the manner of" these styles.

This particular relief of an apsara may serve as a good example of an archaizing sculpture in the manner of the Angkor Vat style.

The figure, however, is heavier and less graceful (*cf.* Fig. 20). The craftsmanship, particularly in details, is less good, giving an impression of provincial origins. The face of the apsara relates more to the Bayon style than to that of Angkor Vat, but is fleshier and has less of the Bayon spirituality. There is no sensuous rendering of the body. It is not outlined under the material of the *sarong*, as in Fig. 20, and the torso has less of the voluptuous qualities of the latter figure. The details of the costume, observed closely, also vary slightly. They have a tendency to be more generalized, and there is no textile pattern on the *sarong*. The triple-pointed tiara is typical of the post-Bayon school of sculpture.

Publ.: Handbook of the Collections, Nelson Gallery and Atkins Museum, p. 241.

Nelson-Atkins Gallery, Kansas City, Mo.; Nelson Fund.

61 BUDDHA ENTHRONED
    Post-Bayon style, thirteenth–early fourteenth century
    Bronze; H. 68⅛ in., W. 27¼ in.

The elaborately cast altar with Buddha is a post-Bayon development of the form which we had a chance to study earlier in connection with the Angkor Vat bronze (No. 30). Buddha is seated in the same position, with interlocked legs, but only his left hand is in *dhyāna mudrā* whereas the right one is in *bhumisparsa* or the earth-touching gesture (as in No. 56). It is therefore possible that it refers to the assault by Māra when the meditation of Buddha under the Bodhi tree was interrupted by this demon. Māra, together with other *asuras* may be depicted on the base.

The decorative *torana* supported by two pillars forms a kind of *probhāvali* (nimbus) around Buddha. It is crowned with a highly stylized Bodhi tree, the trunk of which forms the stem for the *triśula* (trident). Around the pillars and the *torana* are represented twenty-four mortal Buddhas with the twenty-fifth one, slightly bigger, above the summit of the arch. The extremely elaborate decoration, once encrusted with inlaid jewels (now missing), and the dramatically decorative effect are characteristic of the best work of the post-Bayon period.

Kimbell Art Foundation, Fort Worth, Texas.

Selected Bibliography

1. Boisselier, Jean. "Garuda dans l'art khmer," *Bulletin de l'École Française d'Extrême-Orient*, XLIV (1947–1950), pp. 55–87.

2. ———. "Réflexions sur l'art de Jayavarman VII," *Bulletin de la Société des Études Indochinoises de Saigon*, XXVII N.S. (1952), pp. 261 ff.

3. ———. "Précisions sur la statuaire du style d'Aṅkor Vāt," *Bulletin de l'École Française d'Extrême-Orient*, XLVI (1952), pp. 227–252.

4. ———. *La statuaire khmère et son évolution.* (*Publications de l'École Française d'Extrême-Orient*, No. XXXVII.) Saigon: 1955.

5. ———. "Vajrapāṇi dans l'art du Bayon," *Proceedings of the 22nd Congress of Orientalists, Istanbul, 1951* (*Communications*, Vol. II). Leiden: 1957, pp. 324–332.

6. ———. "Un torse khmer du Musée Oriental de Venise," *Artibus Asiae*, XXIII/3–4 (1960), pp. 233–238.

7. ———. *Le Cambodge.* (*Manuel d'Archéologie d'Extrême-Orient*, Pt. I: *Asie du Sud-Est*, Vol. I.) Paris: 1966.

8. ———. "Notes sur l'art du bronze dans l'ancien Cambodge," *Artibus Asiae*, XXIX/4 (1967), pp. 275–334.

9. Briggs, Lawrence P. "The Ancient Khmer Empire," *Transactions of the American Philosophical Society*. XLI, Pt. 1 (1951).

10. Coedès, George. "Bronzes khmers," *Ars Asiatica*, V (1923).

11. ———. "The Central Image of the Bayon of Angkor Thom," *Journal of the Indian Society of Oriental Art*, II (1934), pp. 8 ff.

12. ———. "Le portrait dans l'art khmer," *Arts Asiatiques*, VII/3 (1960), pp. 179–198.

13. Coedès, George, and Dupont, Pierre. "Les inscriptions du Prasat Kok Po," *Bulletin de l'École Française d'Extrême-Orient*, XXXVII (1937), pp. 379–413.

14. Coomaraswamy, Ananda K. "Catalogue des pièces khmères conservées dans les musées de l'Amérique du Nord," *Arts et Archéologie Khmers*, II (1925), pp. 235–240.

15. Coral Rémusat, Gilberte de. *Les arts de l'Indochine.* Paris: 1938.

16. ———. *L'art khmer.* Paris: 1940, 2nd ed. 1951.

17. ———. "Le procédé des emprunts aux styles passés dans l'art khmer," *Arts Asiatiques*, I/2 (1954), pp. 118–128.

18. Dupont, Pierre. "L'art du Kulên et les débuts de la statuaire angkorienne," *Bulletin de l'École Française d'Extrême-Orient*, XXXVI (1936), pp. 415–426.

19. ———. "Les Buddha sur nāga dans l'art khmer," *Artibus Asiae*, XIII/1–2 (1950), pp. 39–62.

20. ———. "La statuaire préangkorienne," *Artibus Asiae*, Suppl. XV (1955).

21. Finot, Louis. "Lokeçvara en Indochine," *Études Asiatiques*, I (1925), pp. 227 ff.

22. Frédéric, Louis. *The Art of Southeast Asia.* New York: 1965.

23. Giteau, Madeleine. *Guide du Musée National de Phnom-Penh, Vol. I: Sculpture.* Phnom-Penh: 1960.

24. ———. *Khmer Sculpture and the Angkor Civilization.* New York: 1965.

25. Groslier, Bernard P., and Arthaud, Jacques. *The Arts and Civilization of Angkor.* New York: 1957.

26. ———. *Indochina.* Cleveland: 1966.

27. Groslier, George. *Recherches sur les Cambodgiens d'après les textes et les monuments depuis les premiers siècles de notre ère.* Paris: 1921.

28. ———. "L'art du bronze au Cambodge," *Arts et Archéologie Khmers*, I (1921–1923), pp. 413–423.

29. ———. "Troisièmes recherches sur les Cambodgiens," *Arts et Archéologie Khmers*, II (1924), pp. 81–112.

30. ———. *Angkor.* Paris: 1924.

31. ———. "Introduction à l'étude des arts khmers," *Arts et Archéologie Khmers*, II (1925), pp. 167–234.

32. ———. *La Sculpture Khmère Ancienne.* Paris: 1925.

33. ———. "Les collections khmères du Musée Albert Sarraut à Phnom Penh," *Ars Asiatica*, XVI (1931).

34. Lunet de Lajonquière, Étienne. *Inventaire descriptif des Monuments du Cambodge.* (*Publications de l'École Française d'Extrême-Orient*, Nos. 4, 8, 9.) Paris: 1902–1911.

35. Mus, Paul. "Angkor in the Time of Jayavarman VII," *Indian Art and Letters*, XI N.S./2 (1937), pp. 65–75.

36. Parmentier, Henri. *L'Art khmer primitif.* 2 vols. (*Publications de l'École Française d'Extrême-Orient*, Nos. XXI, XXII.) Paris: 1927.

37. ———. "History of Khmer Architecture," *Eastern Art*, III (1931).

38. ———. *L'art khmer classique.* 2 vols. (*Publications de l'École Française d'Extrême-Orient*, Nos. XXIX, XXIX bis.) Paris: 1939.

39. Stern, Philippe. *Le Bayon d'Angkor et l'évolution de l'art khmer.* (*Annales du Musée Guimet, Bibl. de Vulgarisation*, Vol. XLVII.) Paris: 1927.

40. ———. "Le style du Kulên," *Bulletin de l'École Française d'Extrême-Orient*, XXXVIII (1938/1939), pp. 111–149 and pls.

41. ———. *Les monuments khmers du style du Bayon et Jayavarman VII.* (*Publications du Musée Guimet, Recherches et Documents d'Art et d'Archéologie*, No. IX.) Paris: 1965.

Catalogue designed and edited by Virginia Field, Assistant Director, Asia House Gallery.

We are gratefully indebted to Yves Coffin, Josephine Powell, and Elizabeth Lyons for the use of their photographs, taken *in situ:* Black and white text illustrations, Figs. 1, 2, 3, 4, 5, 8, 13, 14, 16, and 19 are by Yves Coffin; Figs. 6, 7, 9, 12, 17, 18, and 20 are by Josephine Powell; Figs. 10 and 11 are by Elizabeth Lyons.

Color photographs Nos. 1 and 8 are by Otto E. Nelson; No. 19 is by Donald Wiegel; No. 31 is by Leonard Nones; No. 61 is by Robert Wharton.

Printed and bound at The Curwen Press Ltd., London, England